The Catty-Corner Conversations:

Fifty Dialogues With The Diagonally Opposed

Recording: Michael H. Cole
Editing: Michael H. Cole
Design: Michael H. Cole

THE
CONVERSATIONS

INTRODUCTION TO THE THIRD EDITION

It is difficult to put into words just how unnecessary this introduction of mine should be, and though I am both aware and an acceptor of that maxim that to be heard is to be misheard, I never anticipated being party to the proof's extreme being so proven in a matter so obvious.

It has now been roughly one year since I began sharing with the world my recordings of my conversations with my catty-corner neighbor. These recordings were initially made only for my own amusement, but as I began to make fun of my neighbor to friends, I found it necessary to start sharing his actual words since that seemed to be the only way to convince anyone that he actually existed. It is worth noting that, in these first rounds of sharing, there was not a single instance of confusion that I am able to recall, and every friend whom I shared the conversations with was able to immediately discern that the collection was a humorous thing and that my neighbor was meant to be laughed at.

However, as the interest in mocking my neighbor grew, I was obliged to begin typing up the choicest of our conversations, and this led to their first public posting of one year ago. It makes me sorry to be forced to admit that the waves of misunderstanding began crashing almost immediately, and the very day of their first posting was, in fact, the first day that saw me receive a message from a stranger inquiring further about my neighbor's ideas. The misinterpretations then continued to mount in the days and weeks that followed, and if it were not for a happy few who have so clearly seen through my neighbor and notified me of such then I should think that every reader in the world had gone crazy.

In light of the above, it is my intention to here provide a few facts that should be sufficient to dam any continued confusion. These points, however, should not be regarded as a complete listing of all the ways in which a reader can know my neighbor as wrong. Instead, the following should be regarded as a simple listing of the more obvious of those reasons, and it is to be hoped that the placing of my neighbor in his proper light will be enough to ensure that no further readers are attracted to any of his empty beacons.

First, it must be noted that our conversations are titled by me, not my neighbor. There are many readers, it seems, who assume that the contents of our conversations will be as weighty as their titles indicate, and they thus begin reading under the false impression that weightiness is to be demonstrated. This misconception is the one that I feel most responsible for as it seems to have resulted from my naiveite, and I wish to here make it clear that my neighbor has no hand at all in the production of our conversations. In fact, unless he has heard of them from elsewhere, my neighbor is not aware of my recordings at all.

Secondly, the reader should note that our conversations all end the same way, and though there may be moments when my neighbor wins quippy battles, I clearly win every war. This besting of my neighbor can be most definitively seen within the conversations themselves, but it is also made obvious by the fact that I am the one who always gets the last word in. To some readers, this point may seem minor, but my neighbor is one of those who tries to dominate everything and is never willing to concede, so his being unable to control that which he desires to must be seen as a sure sign of his losing.

Thirdly, it cannot be overstated how much my neighbor is benefited by this particular medium. Any reader who was, for example, allowed to hear my neighbor speak would never be tempted by him, and this would be even more true of any reader able to actually watch him speak. Words on a page do, after all, tend to appear more official and legitimate than they would otherwise, and this does not even factor in my neighbor's habit of both yelling and spitting while he yells as well as his frequent use of verbal abuse. The accoutrements of my neighbor's character are thus largely obscured to the reader, and it is easy to read his words while missing those disqualifiers, which seems to be what has happened to many readers. It is, therefore, incumbent on the reader to keep in mind that a person actually voiced the ideas that will be read and that their words were spoken far more harshly and in a far more insulting manner than they appear.

Lastly, it is worthwhile to note the result that my neighbor's ideas have brought upon himself. Our conversations do, after all, end with our words, so it is understandable that the reader does not readily think beyond them, but this only means that the most gullible of readers will fall into my neighbor's same pitfalls without so much as being aware of them. It is, therefore, in the reader's interest to know that my neighbor has lost every friend whom he has ever had due to his behavior and the unacceptability of his views, and I am, in fact, the only person left in our entire neighborhood who is still willing to speak to him at all. This last point should in no way be taken as a threat against any reader who might find himself interested in the ideas of my neighbor but rather as a warning of where that curiosity will lead.

There are, of course, a near never-ending number of points that could be added to the above list, but their intention, as previously stated, is only to point out the most obvious of signposts, and it remains the reader's job to go forth wary of further ones. With this purpose in mind, I wish to end this introduction with the general reminder that my neighbor is wrong in everything that he says, and there are, in fact, many instances when it is obvious that he is wrong on purpose. All any reader need to do, therefore, is honestly read the transcripts that I have provided, and it will become obvious to him that my neighbor is nothing more than a callous and deeply antisocial man who is angry at the world as well as bitter about the life that he has led in it.

As an additional measure to further help the reader, I have included in this edition some conversations that I had previously filed away as being either too heinous or senseless to share, and I pledge to do the same in the future.

M.H.C.
Nov 2020

ON BEING

Me: Evening, neighbor.

My Catty-Corner Neighbor: Good evening. What are you doing out so late?

Me: I was going to ask you the same thing.

Catty-Corner: I cannot sleep. I have never been one able to get to sleep easily, so coming out and looking at the stars is a way to make myself tired.

Me: They sure do make one feel small.

Catty-Corner: They remind me that nothing is large.

Me: […]

Catty-Corner: […]

Me: Do you know any of the constellations?

Catty-Corner: I do not. They are not real, so I never cared.

Me: Well, I suppose that you could say that about anything.

Catty-Corner: What do you mean?

Me: I mean that you could say that you were not sure about the existence of anything. That excludes yourself, of course.

Catty-Corner: Why am I excluded from all else?

Me: Well, because of *I think therefore I am*.

Catty-Corner: What do that mean?

Me: Have you never heard it before?

Catty-Corner: I did not say that. I asked what it means.

Me: Well, it is difficult to explain. Do you really not know it? Everyone does.

Catty-Corner: Well, if you so surely know it then you should have no issue easily expressing it. Of course, if you are actually just trying to—

Me: *I think therefore I am* means that I am able to doubt everything except myself. It is possible, after all, that my whole life could be a dream, or I could be stuck inside a simulation that is itself inside a simulation, but these things do not matter as far as determining my existence. If all is a dream then I must still exist as the dreamer, and if all is a simulation then I must still exist as the victim. To contemplate your existence, in other words, is to prove it.

Catty-Corner: Does that mean that thinking is separate from everything else?

Me: Of course. It is the thing that is there and by—

Catty-Corner: That does not make any sense at all. Are you just thinking out loud?

Me: This is something that everyone is supposed to know, and I should not even have to be telling it to you. Did you never pay attention in school? I bet that you did not.

Catty-Corner: I did not do so in the right way, I suppose. Do you really believe that a mind thinking is any more mystical than a heart beating?

Me: If you mean just your *physical* brain then I am talking about something different. Thinking is something separate, which is what I just said. You have to—

Catty-Corner: That does not make any sense at all, though, which is what I just said. You should find some system of doubt to apply to your words before speaking them. After all, if myself as a thinking thing could be the only existing thing then how is it that I could ever be able to produce a thought?

Me: What do you mean?

Catty-Corner: Well, if you do not eat then you cannot think, and it is as simple as that. You cannot doubt your head without also doubting your mind. If the bread that you are chewing on is not real then neither is your mind because that bread is what allows your mind to think. No thought, after all, was ever fired without fuel, and if a needle was able to be stuck into your head to suck out all the energy that it currently has stored then your mind would instantly be put into a state incapable of thought. How could it even be *possible* for your mind to be the only thing that is real when it has requirements for its own existence?

Me: You are obviously having trouble with this, and I am not sure how much simpler I can make it. I may not have told it to you in the correct way, but the point is that you can be sure about your existence while not being able to be sure about anything else, so that is what is important.

Catty-Corner: It is not true, though. You do not exist any more than does the United States.

Me: The United States does exist.

Catty-Corner: Does it? What is its mass?

Me: Well, I am not sure. I would say—

Catty-Corner: How about its color? Can you tell me its texture?

Me: What do you mean?

Catty-Corner: I mean that the United States is an aggregate that gives the impression of oneness when viewed from particular distances, and a person is the same thing. You do not exist and are merely a semblance of component parts just as the United States does not exist and is merely a semblance of Americans. Consciousness is like the country in that both can be investigated and determined to be nothing more than terms arbitrarily applied to any number of separate and individually named actors. A collection that acts in concert gives the illusion of literal union, and this is what we are. There is, therefore, no such thing as character besides that which is created. There is, therefore, no such thing as inborn besides that which is imbedded. There is, therefore, no such—

Me: You do not even *sound* like you are trying to convince me.

Catty-Corner: Do you mean that you do not like the implications of the argument? It is important to remember that existence does not have to be sifted through you before becoming legitimate, and if your reasoning results in what is pleasing then it is most likely appeasing.

Me: If nothing else then I would think that the potential—

Catty-Corner: There is quite a word. *Potential* is a word that is obviously full of it. One might marvel at the—

Me: It is obvious that you have not been listening to me at all. If you are only just—

Catty-Corner: Let me make my point.

Me: Not if you are not going to let me make mine. You have not been, or you have not been paying attention, or—

Catty-Corner: Let me make my final point, and then I will be done. The truth is that nothing can ever be said to contain more *potential* for consciousness than a polished credenza. What, after all, is that wooden buffet along your dining room wall but a particular configuration of energy happening to not result in thought, and what are you but a particular configuration of energy happening to result in thought? A mere *change* would be needed to give that credenza thought. It already consists of the required materials, which means that it could be said to be at all times at the doorstep of a reorganization into sentience. *Everything*, in fact, already has all the pieces, but they are just very rarely in the perfectly right place. Arrangement alone distinguishes one thing from another, and how many—

Me: This is a waste of time, and I am going back inside. I did not want to stay out all night, anyway.

Catty-Corner: Are you sure? I was hoping that you would have a counterargument.

Me: I really should head back in.

Catty-Corner: Will you tell me what you are before you go?

Me: What do you mean?

Catty-Corner: Well, what are you? If you are certain of yourself then you should, at the very least, be aware of an aspect of yourself.

Me: I am standing right in front of you. Are you really as blind as you are stupid?

Catty-Corner: What I see cannot be what you are, though. If, for example, we were to say that you are a headed, four-limbed torso then what would we say if you were to lose an arm? Would we be forced to say that you had died?

Me: Of course not.

Catty-Corner: Would we say that what you had actually been all along was a headed, three-limbed torso?

Me: Of course not.

Catty-Corner: Then what would happen when you lost another limb and then another? What about when you lost one piece of your brain and then another? What is your existence other than your insistence, and what is it that could not be cut away from you without splitting you? What, in other words, is you indivisible? If, for example, we were—

Me: I really should head back in. You should, too. It is late.

Catty-Corner: Can we continue our conversation in the morning?

Me: I might be able to. I have to be up and out early, though. I have a busy day.

Catty-Corner: Can we plan on another day?

Me: I will have to let you know.

ON EXPERIENCE

Me: Morning, neighbor.

My Catty-Corner Neighbor: Good morning. You are up and about earlier than usual.

Me: It is just a change. I am trying something new today.

Catty-Corner: Is that so?

Me: I am going rock climbing. I read an article about it, and I made the decision right away.

Catty-Corner: You read an article about rock climbing?

Me: Well, the article itself was about philosophy.

Catty-Corner: […]

Me: It is a new philosophy, and it is a rather sobering one, too. It forces you to look at yourself, acknowledge that you only have one unique and precious life, then address what you want that life to be about. It is about doing new and greater things. It is difficult, but the philosophy forces you to fill your life with everything that you are able to.

Catty-Corner: It sounds like quite the philosophy.

Me: It is. I did not have time to read the entire article about it, but I did not see a single negative comment below it. Most people do not realize the amount of accumulations that we all leave on the table. The philosophy really is rather sobering.

Catty-Corner: I can imagine. I did not know that you were a climber, though.

Me: Well, I am not. It is going to be entirely new to me.

Catty-Corner: If it were me then I think that I would be somewhat scared.

Me: I am more anxious than scared, I suppose. I am keeping myself steady, though. It is important to remember that philosophy is not for the weak-willed.

Catty-Corner: That may, in fact, be true. You are not going to take a class on rock climbing first, though?

Me: Well, experience is the best teacher.

Catty-Corner: What do you mean?

Me: I mean that doing something is the best way to learn it. Everyone knows that.

Catty-Corner: Do you really believe that?

Me: Well, everyone does.

Catty-Corner: Does that mean that you can explain it to me?

Me: Do you need me to?

Catty-Corner: That was not my question.

Me: I know that you are trying to lead me into some stupid trap, but I will not let you. You always act like I must follow along to wherever you want to go into whatever you want to talk about, and I sometimes think that you actually think of the whole universe as revolving around yourself, and the rest of us are just characters for your circumstances. I really do think that of you, and it is your own fault. You consider your own eyes to be—

Catty-Corner: If experience is such an encompassing teacher then why does it have such a narrow curriculum? Will you tell me that?

Me: What do you mean?

Catty-Corner: Well, what does experience teach but itself? What *can* experience teach but itself? Is experience, for example, not like the history teacher who is only able to lecture on his own life, and would it not be fair to expect such a teacher to be fired upon his first review?

Me: I see what you mean, I suppose. You are being too literal, though, which is what you always do. If nothing else then experience brings familiarity, which can be a test for assumptions.

Catty-Corner: Well, *familiarity* is often the most blinding factor of all. You are looking at things too simply, which is what you always do. Stop trying to come up with an answer for me, and, instead, direct yourself fully at the question.

Me: Well, what is the question? I bet that you do not even—

Catty-Corner: What type of teacher is experience? *That* is the question.

Me: I already told you that, though. Experience is the best of teachers, which is something that everyone knows. Just because you can maybe argue that it is not a perfect teacher does not mean that it is a worthless one.

Catty-Corner: Does that mean that an education of experience alone would be the best of all possible?

Me: I did not say that. A person would obviously not want to have an education based *solely* on experience. It would, in fact, be—

Catty-Corner: How would that be possible?

Me: What do you mean?

Catty-Corner: How would it be possible for one's education to not be based *solely* on experience?

Me: You should be the one telling me that. Why do I have to tell you your own argument?

Catty-Corner: We have not yet reached my argument, and we are, instead, still working our way through yours. You have said that experience is the best teacher, which is a claim needing proof. You have also said that experience should not be one's sole teacher, which is a claim needing proof. We should look at the second claim first, which—

Me: Well, the second claim is the easier of the two because it is obvious. No one would say that experience should be any person's only teacher. For some things, of course, a person would obviously be better off trying to learn about them rather than trying to experience them.

Catty-Corner: How would a person do that?

Me: By opening a book, for example.

Catty-Corner: Would this act itself not be an experience?

Me: Do you mean that I would be experiencing the book?

Catty-Corner: That is a fair way of putting it. After all, a book written in 1801 is not read the same way in the years 1901 or 2001, and the same applies to a book read in poor weather as opposed to if it were read during a picnic on a sunny day. Perhaps, for example, you were to read the greatest book of all time on a day in which you were in a foul mood, or you read a cliche love story just after a breakup, or you read the work of one great thinker while already being a disciple of his rival, or you read a particular sentence while tired, or giddy, or depressed, or angry, or in any other imaginable state. The truth is that no information can ever come to you in a way other than experience. There is no destined or proper way in which information makes its way into you, and there is no destined or proper way in which you are to sieve that information. Experience is the only teacher that you will ever have.

Me: If that is true then why are you so opposed to it? You said earlier that experience is the worst of teachers, and now you are saying that it is a person's only one. Which is it?

Catty-Corner: Both are true, and I preach either.

Me: *Both*? That does not make any sense, though. They are on opposite sides of the argument.

Catty-Corner: It makes sense, and it does, in fact, explain a great many things. It does not make your *sensibilities*, however, which is the root of your opposition, of which the fruit will be your unchanged state. You do not like the implications, and such will be enough for you to find shelter in any complications. Experience is, after all, strong enough to smother any found truths of itself. Simply decide that I have expressed things overly meanly, for example, and you will have yourself a nice, warm counterargument to curl up in.

Me: You are just trying to make me look stupid, which only makes you look mean. You said something that did not make any sense, and you insulted me whenever I pointed it out, so I know that you do not actually have anything to say. It never occurs to you that you could be wrong, so you assert anything to make yourself seem—

Catty-Corner: What could I be wrong about? We have still not reached any argument of mine. You made two claims requiring investigation, and that search has led us to where we are. We can say that experience is the narrowest way in which a person can acquire information, and we can also say that experience is the only way in which a person acquires information.

Me: Those cannot both be true, though.

Carry-Corner: Why not?

Me: Well, because they are opposites.

Catty-Corner: Why does that matter?

28

Me: If they are both true then what are we supposed to do? It would mean that we begin things in a hole that we are never able to climb out of.

Catty-Corner: Well, desirability is not an ingredient of actuality. The truth is that experience is a paradox. It is the worst of teachers as well as the only one, and it is the stupid option as well as the smart. There is not a more misleading guide that you could ever have than experience, but there is also no other guide able to make the trek with you. You are tethered to experience like a bad relation, and you will forever remain in its shadow like a famous one. Experience is the only way of learning about the world, and experience is the most warped way of learning about the world. The greatest lies that you will ever have the chance to face will be within yourself, and it is, therefore, obvious that—

Me: Just because you think that you have proved something does not mean that I have to change my mind.

Catty-Corner: Well, would you share your counterargument with me? That way, I will know it, too.

Me: I do not have to. I am already late now, anyway. I am trying to do something new, and you have me late like usual. You probably would not even listen to me.

Catty-Corner: I promise that I will.

Me: I know that you would not, so your promise means nothing to me. You can say that you would listen, but anyone would say that. It is easy to say things when you do not concern yourself with backing them up.

Catty-Corner: I see. Well, I await your counterargument.

Me: I am sure that you will.

Catty-Corner: Will I see you tomorrow?

Me: I am not sure. I have a busy day, and I may want to go rock climbing again, too.

ON HUMANITY

Me: Evening, neighbor.

My Catty-Corner Neighbor: Good evening. You look like you must have had a great day. Did something exciting happen?

Me: Not only did I have a great day, but I have physical proof of it that I can show to you. My membership card finally arrived in the mail, and I have it with me. It was supposed to get here a few days ago, but I have it now, so that is what is important. I can now call myself a bona fide humanitarian.

Catty-Corner: What do you mean?

Me: There is a nonprofit organization that I often donate money to, and they have levels for their donors. I was at the *Friend* level for all last year, but my most recent donation was a big one, and it rose me up to the *Humanitarian* level.

Catty-Corner: What are the responsibilities of the level?

Me: Well, there are not any. It is a giving organization, so I have never actually even been to wherever their physical location is. If you stop donating enough then you will fall out of the level, of course, so that is one responsibility of it, I suppose.

Catty-Corner: What are the perks of the level?

Me: I already told you that. They sent me a new membership card to replace my old one. It is the size of a business card, and you are supposed to put it in your wallet so that you can whip it out whenever you need to. It has my name on it, of course, and then it says that *this card shall be taken as proof of the above-named individual's status as a Humanitarian, as certified by—*

Catty-Corner: What is a humanitarian?

Me: Have you not been listening to me at all? *Humanitarian* is the next level after *Friend*.

Catty-Corner: What is the definition of the word, though? Is it, for example, something that you can point out to me?

Me: Do you really want me to point to myself? If you need me to then I will, but it will just make you look stupid since I already told—

Catty-Corner: What about before it was you? It may be true that the word is synonymous with your existence, but if you admit that it is something that you have attained then it must have once been a gain, which means that it has a prior history of its own that cannot, by rule, have anything to do with you. The world has existed for longer than you have, after all, so the aspects of it must, at the very least, have some virgin state from before your—

Me: Everyone knows what a humanitarian is. They are people who help, and they—

Catty-Corner: Do you mean that they help themselves?

Me: Of course not. Humanitarians help other people, and if you are really—

Catty-Corner: That is not true.

Me: What do you mean?

Catty-Corner: Humanitarians do not help people. Instead, a humanitarian is someone who helps *humans*. There is a difference between the two, and it is a very important distinction. All humans are people but not all people are humans in that same way that all squares are rectangles but not all rectangles are squares. The word *human*, in other words, has a stricter definition, and the word is, in fact, most historically comparable to the word *roman* since their arcs are—

Me: There is a difference between you and me, and *that* is the very important distinction here. To hear you suggest what you are suggesting may be the worst thing that you have ever said.

Catty-Corner: What am I suggesting?

Me: What do you mean?

Catty-Corner: Well, what is it that I am suggesting? I have so far only cleared up two definitions. I said that humanitarians are those who help humans, and then I was saying that a human is defined by membership in humanity, which means that—

Me: You are saying that people are not humans.

Catty-Corner: I am saying that *some*, by rule, cannot be. After all, how could there be those who are charged with *crimes against humanity* while still being regarded as members in it? They must, I think, have first been outside the border before having been able to attack its innards. What about thinking things, too?

Me: What do you mean?

Catty-Corner: Well, a thinking thing is someone who denies the definite existence of everything but himself, and this means that such a person cannot also be a human. How *could* he be, after all? If we agree that a human is defined by membership in humanity and that a thinking thing is someone who cannot, by rule, accept the definite existence of others then how, therefore, could a thinking thing ever be a member of *anything*?

Me: I will not continue to stand here and listen to you spew hate. You sound like Nazi propaganda, which is what I knew was going to happen whenever you brought up *crimes against humanity*, but I was stupid and let—

Catty-Corner: The truth is that you may like to think of yourself as the squasher of what those Germans did, but you are, in fact, their poorly-written sequel. Those nationalists had their superhumans, and we have our suprahumans. They adopted an overcoming, and we have decided on a preponderance. The former killed millions, and the latter is ruining billions. It will be interesting to see which of the two the future decides to have had a worse—

Me: You are so obviously wrong that it makes me feel sick to even look at you. That you could ever advance an idea that is so intentionally harmful is something that—

Catty-Corner: If you ever find yourself feeling sorry for thinking things then any amount of honest reflection should be enough to convince you otherwise.

Me: What do you mean?

Catty-Corner: Well, why would anyone ever feel sorry for them when they would never do the same? They *cannot* do the same, after all, and it is an actual inability on their part. They do not regard you as having the same grounding in existence that they regard themselves as having, so you cannot matter to them on the same level that they matter to themselves. It is important to remember that each thinking thing regards himself as actuality's arbiter, and even the most kind-hearted of thinking things runs into this dilemma, and they are only able to escape by—

Me: I think that I am going to—

Catty-Corner: Let me make my final point before you go. Empathy is often discussed as a thing that the world has begun ignoring, but it is, in fact, a thing that the world has become incapable of, and it has been feebly replaced by pity. There is a difference between the two, and it is a very important distinction. *Pity* is simply feeling sad about the shoes that another is forced to wear, but *empathy* is the imagining of oneself in those shoes. Empathy is, in other words, the attempt to *understand* that which one sees rather than the visceral and transient reaction to it. After all, how *could* a thinking thing ever actually imagine himself in another's shoes when the very core of him states that those other shoes are not, by rule, as legitimate as his own? It is thus not that thinking things do not practice empathy but rather that they lack the equipment necessary for it. The only hope for humanity will be for the remaining humans of the world to unite, and it will be their burden to make the difficult but undamning decision of finally denying communion to those whose very aim states that there is nothing wrong with draining the whole—

Me: I have waited long enough. I will be—

Catty-Corner: Will you tell me how you know that I am wrong? If a human *must* be a member of humanity, and if a thinking thing *must* admit that nothing but himself can be—

Me: You are wrong at your very core, I think.

Catty-Corner: I see.

Me: I hope that it will be a while before I see you again.

ON PURPOSE

Me: Afternoon, neighbor.

My Catty-Corner Neighbor: Good afternoon. I was not expecting to see you until late this evening.

Me: Well, I had all those plans, but I just could not make myself get going today. I woke up, and I knew right away that I had no chance. The whole world seemed gray the very minute that I opened my eyes.

Catty-Corner: It was rather sunny this morning, I think.

Me: What does *that* have to do with anything? I am talking about something important, not just whatever state the world happens to be in. I woke up, and it felt as if there was a gigantic weight on me. It is like the universe was conspiring against me all through the night.

Catty-Corner: Do you feel sick?

Me: Only in my soul.

Catty-Corner: What do you mean?

Me: I just do not get the point of anything. What is the point in getting up and running around all day if I am

38

just going to end up back in my same bed that night? It is like running on a track and exhausting yourself to only return to where you started.

Catty-Corner: Well, life is about more than getting your daily lollipop.

Me: That is not what I am saying at all. All you ever try to do is find some way to make me look stupid, and you do not realize how bad it makes you look. I am not talking about just today, either. It is a feeling that I have had many times.

Catty-Corner: Well, life is about more than getting your lifely lollipop.

Me: Are you too stupid to understand what I am telling you? I think that you might actually be. I am talking about the purpose of life, not lollipops. There must be some deeper meaning to everything. I know that there must be an answer. Things could not just—

Catty-Corner: Have you tried walking into a church? They will be able to find something for you to do with yourself, I bet.

Me: That is not what I am talking about at all. I want to know the purpose of life, not just what some person thinks that I should do with it. The things that you say are sometimes so stupid that it—

Catty-Corner: The truth is not that you cannot find a purpose but, instead, that you cannot find a purpose that you like, which is a very different thing. There are, in fact, too *many* purposes flitting about the world rather than too few. What you want is—

Me: If anyone is *wanting* then it is you, not me. You just want to make me look wrong and feel bad about myself, and the only weapon that you have is to insult me, which is all you ever do. You have not said anything that even makes sense, anyway.

Catty-Corner: My point is that you are looking for definite purpose rather than just purpose, which complicates matters greatly. There are a great many things that will gladly receive the commitment of your life, after all, but you want to know that whatever step you take today will not be able to be questioned tomorrow. You do not want an answer, but, instead, you want *the* answer. It is certainty that you want, and the fact that you can never have it makes you prejudiced against anything less than it. You also, however, want a purpose of life that does not include your wasted life. In other words, you want a purpose that applies to all while most definitively still including you. Well, there is no such thing. Existence predates you, after all, so no definite purpose of life can *ever* contain any concern for your own life, which—

Me: How is this supposed to help me? The one thing that I told you was that I am having a bad day, and all you think to do is to try to make it worse. You are supposed to help someone when they need help, not just tell him whatever you want to hear yourself. I am going back inside. I knew that it was stupid to try—

Catty-Corner: Let me make my point before you go. All I wanted to say is that if you want something inarguable rather than just a choice of the best arguments then you will have to find something that roots itself in the most basic of matters. That which is both ever-present and ever-overarching must, after all, have very sound footing. What you will find is that existence at its most bare is one thing crashing into another and thereby sparking something that could not have resulted from either without the collision. In other words, the purpose of life can be said to be the identification and elevation of lesser life, which means—

Me: What exactly is *lesser* supposed to mean?

Catty-Corner: It means its meaning, which also seems to mean that it is mean. Stop believing that taking offense is in any way valid defense. You never actually listen to me but only listen for whatever you might be able to turn around and use against me. You are so always on the attack that your sole defense has become this blatant and shameless deafness to all but what could be of immediate use to you for your own cannons. You hear *lesser*, and you think *fodder*. It is all so far beyond any form of classical embarrassment that there should—

Me: The only one who should be embarrassed is you. I wish that you could actually see yourself right now. You would be just as disgusted as I am. I tried to tell you my problems, and you made everything about yourself, which is no different than your usual, selfish self. I am not even going to let you say another word to me. You have ruined my whole day, which is what you wanted the whole time, I bet.

ON EQUALITY

Me: Morning, neighbor.

My Catty-Corner Neighbor: Good morning. It is good to see you. Is today the day?

Me: It is. All those other worthless days have finally given way.

Catty-Corner: It is nice to see you so excited. It makes me excited, in fact. Joy really is more infectious than all but a very few diseases.

Me: Well, that infectiousness is going around. You are getting it from me then amplifying it for me. It makes me even more excited to be causing excitement.

Catty-Corner: When should things be finished and ready?

Me: Well, all things being equal then it should be done by tonight.

Catty-Corner: I see. Would tomorrow be a more reasonable estimate?

Me: What do you mean? If it is not until tomorrow then it will mean that something went wrong.

Catty-Corner: Well, that is good. I must have misheard you. You must have said that all things remaining *unequal* then it should be done by tonight.

Me: I know what I said. It is an expression. Have you never heard it before? It means that if nothing changes then everything should be ready by tonight.

Catty-Corner: Does that mean that it will be ready by tomorrow?

Me: What do you mean?

Catty-Corner: Well, an unchanged state is an impossible one.

Me: Is that really a point that you have to make right now? I do not understand why you get enjoyment from trying to confuse me.

Catty-Corner: I am only trying to figure out what you are saying. I am confused myself, and I have not been trying to make any point at all.

Me: I am *sure* that that is true.

Catty-Corner: Well, I apologize for paying so much attention to your words. I often forget how much doing so undermines you.

Me: You have not undermined me at all. The only thing that you are *under* is sense, and I hope that you run into a mine. All you do is attack people and try to find one little, unimportant way in which they are wrong, and then you act like you have actually made an argument.

Catty-Corner: Well, I would admit that it is true that lack of argument is my most common argument.

Me: That is a *perfect* example. You even act like it is something to be proud of.

Catty-Corner: Well, I do not see why I should be blamed for the voids in others, even if I become the first to stumble across them. Discoverers often have their discoveries named after them, which I would not be against, but they are, after all, rarely blamed for the fact of what they discover. If your argument unravels before it even fully leaves your mouth then it is your own fault for not taking the time to properly stitch it. If an argument is put forward then I do not see why it should not be put through its paces. After all, my reality should not have to be a product of your sentimentality in the same way that your discomfort should not have to be my disqualification.

Me: Is all this just because I said the word *equal*? Are you really going to take a position against equality then expect me to listen to you?

Catty-Corner: My expectation is usually that I will be ignored, despised, and laughed at by whomever I am with. However, when away from me and thus willing to think about my arguments then the person will find their holds to be sound, no matter how hard he tries to pry them. After a long enough time has passed then whatever argument I made will sink into the person and become just another aspect of his worldview, and the person will find some other face to apply to the origin of the argument so that I can remain the thing that was ignored, despised, and laughed at. *That* is my expectation.

Me: If that is your expectation then why will you not change? Have you ever thought of the fact that if everyone thinks that you are wrong then you might actually be so?

Catty-Corner: I think that very thing every day. In fact, I usually assume that I am wrong, and then such leads me to being right.

Me: I always assume that you are wrong, too.

Catty-Corner: You always assume yourself to be right. There is a difference between the two, and it is a very important distinction. You could, however, say that you always assume that I am wrong by way of always assuming that I am going to be opposed to you, which makes it so that—

Me: The only one of us who makes assumptions all the time is you. You even make ones that no one else ever would, and you make them every day, too. I bet that you are against equality just because you realized that no one else is.

Catty-Corner: Does that mean that you are pro-equality?

Me: Of course. You do not even need to call it that since everyone is for it.

Catty-Corner: Does that mean that you are able to tell me what equality is?

Me: Have you never seen an equals sign?

Catty-Corner: Does that mean that it is a mathematical equality that you are talking about rather than an actual one?

Me: Of course not. They are obviously the same, and it—

Catty-Corner: What, for example, would happen if I were to write the simple math equation of *one equals one* on a piece of paper?

Me: What do you mean?

Catty-Corner: Well, what would you say? Would you say that it was true, or false, or that not enough information has been provided for you to—

Me: I would say that it was true, of course.

Catty-Corner: In what way?

Me: In the way that one equals one. You do not even need to use a formula or anything like that.

Catty-Corner: One equals one in a mathematical way?

Me: Of course.

Catty-Corner: What about the *literal* way?

Me: What do you mean?

Catty-Corner: Well, it should be obvious that the ones drawn on either side of the equals sign could never actually be equal. After all, what if I happened to draw one of them taller than the other? What if the base of the left one was made fatter than the right, or what if the ink in my pen slightly gave out while—

Me: Those differences are not important. We are talking about equality.

Catty-Corner: Is it possible for any difference to not alter equality? Each and every difference *must* matter, I think, since there—

Me: That does not make any sense at all. If it were true then you would have to say that another distinction between the drawn ones would be that you had to make one of them before the other, which is obviously ridiculous.

Catty-Corner: What do you mean?

Me: Well, it would be stupid to say that the one drawn first is unequal with the one drawn second simply because they could not have happened at exactly the same time.

Catty-Corner: Why is that?

Me: Well, what difference does it make? In what way would it be better or worse to have been first?

Catty-Corner: Well, I am not sure. I would say—

Me: How can you not be sure when this is your own argument? Does that mean that you are not sure of what you are saying but that you will not let it hamper your conviction in the slightest since you are so—

Catty-Corner: I do not have to fully comprehend a distinction to be aware of its existence. The knowledge of an answer is not a requirement for the initial cognizance of that answer, and I do not, therefore, have to know which of the drawn ones is better to know that one of them *must*, by rule, be. It may even be true that I am incapable of ever distinguishing between the two ones, but that still does not matter as far as their actual equality. The world does not await our awareness, after all, and I do not have to be able to name a distinction for it to exist in the same way that gravity did not have to peek out from behind a corner while hoping that Newton would finally notice the falling apple. Just because I may not be able to clearly see a thing does not mean that a more complete view of it does not exist, and a point, after all, need not be comprehensive to be incisive. The truth is that any position in the universe is distinct from all other positions, and it must, therefore, be better or worse than all those other positions. If you would be willing to just—

Me: The only one of us lacking *will* is you, and I am sure that you are just repeating what some—

Catty-Corner: Are you able to identify for me a single way in which the drawn ones are equal?

Me: Well, they are obviously the same, which is what I have been telling you this whole time, and—

Catty-Corner: Same is not equal, and *never* let anyone blend the two in your mind. If you step outside of math class then one does not equal one, so distinction, therefore, always remains, and equality must thus forever remain as distant as heaven.

Me: I think that I have had enough of you for today. It is supposed to be a special day for me, after all, and you are making everything about yourself, which is—

Catty-Corner: Will you share your counterargument with me before you go?

Me: Of course not. You obviously do not care what I think.

Catty-Corner: Will you tell me tomorrow? It will not be as special of a day for you, after all.

Me: Even if it is not special then it will still be too special. I do not like wasting my time telling people things that they should already know and that are obvious.

Catty-Corner: I see.

Me: What you can see is me leaving.

Catty-Corner: Well, I await your counterargument.

Me: Well, you will be doing so for a while, I bet.

ON FAIRNESS

Me: Afternoon, neighbor.

My Catty-Corner Neighbor: Good afternoon. You are back earlier than usual.

Me: Well, I realized that I should stop bothering. In fact, I realized that it is stupid to even think of continuing to do so.

Catty-Corner: What do you mean?

Me: Well, what is the point? That is a good way of putting it, I suppose.

Catty-Corner: Do you mean in general? I was just thinking about the possibility of—

Me: Of course not. I have no trouble coming to terms with that at all. My problem is with finding out that I work for a boss who pays less in taxes than I do. I found out about it today. He is richer than a whole gated cul-de-sac, but he still finds a way to pay the government less each year than I do. If someone else already has the whole thing worked out then what is the point in working? *That* is what I mean.

Catty-Corner: I see.

Me: All I want is for things to be fair.

Catty-Corner: Do you know how much less than you it is that your boss pays in taxes?

Me: That is not important at all, which is something that I should not have to tell you. He is my boss, after all, so he makes more money than I do.

Catty-Corner: Does that mean that he should be taxed more than you?

Me: Of course.

Catty-Corner: Would that be fair?

Me: Of course.

Catty-Corner: I see.

Me: My boss would not have been able to make all that money without the rest of us, after all. He *should* pay more, and there is not anyone who would try to—

Catty-Corner: If your boss were to pay more taxes than you then does that mean that he should get more in return than you do?

Me: What do you mean?

Catty-Corner: Well, should an ambulance, for example, arrive at his home quicker than yours? If he goes before a judge then should that almighty show your boss a preference in proportion to past payments? If you were to—

Me: Of course not. Things like those are the opposites of fairness.

Catty-Corner: What do you mean?

Me: I mean that the government is supposed to treat everyone the same, which is something that everyone knows, and no one would ever be stupid enough to not—

Catty-Corner: If the government is supposed to treat everyone the same then how could it ever tax different individuals different amounts?

Me: I have already told you that. It is fair because it is correcting unfairness. It is not fair that my boss makes more money than I do, after all, so taxes are supposed to inject fairness into the situation.

Catty-Corner: Is charging two amounts for the same thing not, by rule, unfairness in its most obvious?

Me: You are looking at it wrong. This is about people returning what they—

Catty-Corner: The truth is that fairness is the weakest of all persuasion's many lovers in the same way that emotion is the weakest of all her many children. After all, is there anything that is, by rule, less *fair* than the forced unpressing of an advantage? Would *true* fairness not *always* favor the haves over the have-nots? It is important to remember that the most telling sign of unfairness is everyone else being regarded as the same as you.

Me: Well, you may not be rich, but you are certainly their lackey. It would, in fact, not surprise me at all to find out that you were in some way paid by them. You have not been making any sense, anyway, and it is obvious that your only point is to—

Catty-Corner: My point is that you may tax the rich whatever amount that you are able to, but have the decency to not sully the holy habit of fairness in the process. The four-letter word that you should use is *more*, not *fair*. You are willing to profess any creed if it means the consummation of your greed, and you will only meet an overwhelming amount of greed in return. Taxing them more will, after all, only mean that they become more incentivized to hide even more, and it is important to remember that any—

Me: If you are so much smarter than everyone else then what should the tax rate be? You probably just want rich people to spend their whole lives making money and keeping down—

Catty-Corner: Well, if I were to use the principle of giving in return for what has been gotten then I would say that the tax rate's percentage should be somewhere up high in the upper nineties because when it is—

Me: Thank you for confirming for me that I am wasting my time. If your whole plan was only to make a stupid joke then you should have let me know so that I could have not listened to you from the start. My day has been bad enough already, and now I am—

Catty-Corner: Can I finish my point before you go?

Me: Your point was already finished. There is not—

Catty-Corner: I only said half of my point. The other side is that if I were to use the principle of trying to do what is right then I would get rid of income taxing entirely since all it does is disproportionately hinder the lawful, and those are the very *last* people who the government should seek to harm since they are the very last who will stand and—

Me: I am going inside. I have been more than fair with you today, and I know that I have given you more opportunities to have an actual conversation than anyone else would have. They all would have left long before me.

ON NATURE

Me: Evening, neighbor.

My Catty-Corner Neighbor: Good evening. Where is it that you are getting back from? You look like you may have had dinner somewhere nice.

Me: I was visiting a friend at the hospital.

Catty-Corner: I am sorry to hear that.

Me: Thank you for saying so. My visiting him helped, I think.

Catty-Corner: Was it anyone whom I know?

Me: It was a friend of mine from years ago. We went to school together, and we have always tried to stay in touch, but that is, of course, a story that is as old as friendship itself. He got married while we were still in college, and he has three kids now. I had not seen him for four years, at the very least, until today.

Catty-Corner: I hope that it is nothing serious.

Me: Well, *serious* is perhaps not the best word to use since it is, after all, relative. If you mean whether my friend will live then he will, and he will, in fact, make a full recovery.

Catty-Corner: That is good to hear.

Me: […]

Catty-Corner: […]

Me: Did you not hear what I said?

Catty-Corner: What do you mean?

Me: I said that *serious* is not the best word to use.

Catty-Corner: What do you mean?

Me: I mean that the issue will not get him, but the price of the cure is going to. I saw, in other words, how much it is that he is going to have to pay, and it almost made me sick myself. I could hardly believe that it was such a high price, and I am, in fact, worried about a relapse whenever my friend sees the amount for himself.

Catty-Corner: Well, a full recovery does, after all, indicate a certain *fullness*, which would seem to—

Me: That *full* recovery, however, is just going to be back to where my friend already was. He is not getting anything for his money.

Catty-Corner: I see.

Me: It does not sound like you do, which is, I bet, because you have never before been in the situation yourself. You have never had to pay for your own health, so you do not think that it is wrong for others to have to do so.

Catty-Corner: Well, there are, I suppose, a lot of things that people pay for that I do not think that they—

Me: I am not going to let you ramble off into some new point that will not make any sense at all, anyway. I have you trapped, and I will not let you trick yourself free. You are going to have to admit that it is wrong for my friend to have to pay so much for his hospital stay.

Catty-Corner: Well, I would first have to examine the bill itself before even beginning any preliminary verdict. After all, there could be numerous extra—

Me: That is not what we are talking about at all. Everyone knows that it is wrong for my friend to have to pay *any* price, and you are the only person who would ever need to have this explained. It is, after all, a person's health that we are talking about.

Catty-Corner: […]

Me: You cannot remain silent. I will not let you. I am going to make you prove just how wrong it is that you are.

Catty-Corner: Well, can you first tell me why I am wrong? That way, I can more easily be part of everyone else, and we can from there say—

Me: The reason why you are wrong is because no one should have to pay for something that he has a right to. It is, in fact, unamerican.

Catty-Corner: Does that mean that health is a right?

Me: Of course. I am not sure why you are having so much—

Catty-Corner: If health is a right then is sickness a crime?

Me: What do you mean?

Catty-Corner: Well, if, for example, I were to pass to you the flu then would I be criminally responsible for what it does to you? A *right* of yours, after all, will have been trampled upon by me, and a trampled right is that which *must*, by rule, be a crime. Is there perhaps a fine that would be fair, or should I go to prison for the same number of days that you miss of work, or should I be—

Me: What you are saying does not make any sense at all. We are talking about a person having a right to his own health, not sicknesses. *No one* should have to pay for a person's healthcare, and that includes both the person himself and whoever may have accidently hurt him or made him sick.

Catty-Corner: I see.

Me: You would benefit from healthcare being free, anyway. We all would, after all, since we would no longer have to pay for it, so there is not any reason to be against it.

Catty-Corner: What about death?

Me: What do you mean?

Catty-Corner: Well, how could I ever assert a *right* to health while aware of the fact that I will eventually die? If it is that which will inevitably be lost then how can it also be an inviolate right, and does sheer death, after all, not itself disprove any idea of rightful health? The truth is that health is first not a *natural* right because of the existence of death, and it is next not a *legal* right because of its requirement of making sickness a crime.

Me: You are looking at it wrong.

Catty-Corner: Well, will you point me right?

Me: I should not have to. Nature gives to everyone a right to life, which is something that—

Catty-Corner: The truth is that you can *say* that you have a right to life, but nature very obviously disagrees. After all, one's *right* to free speech does not come with a limited number of uses, and one's *right* to religion does not entail only the socially accepted. It is important to remember that you can assert your *right* to life with every moment of your life, but nature will still take that life from you when the time comes.

Me: […]

Catty-Corner: Are you going inside?

Me: I am. I decided, however, that you did not have right to know, so I was going to let—

Catty-Corner: Will you let me make my final point before you go?

Me: Of course not. There is not a more—

Catty-Corner: It is important to remember that rights are not that which we like, want, or think that we can claim. Instead, they are the practical necessities that are required for legitimacy in government. The truth is that you currently posses the *privilege* of life, and there is, in fact, no such thing as a *right* to it at all.

Me: You have never been more wrong about anything.

ON NATURAL

Me: Afternoon, neighbor.

My Catty-Corner Neighbor: Good afternoon. Do you think that you are going to be able to back your car out? It looks like it will be a tight fit.

Me: I am sure that I will be able.

Catty-Corner: Do you want me to come help guide you out? I would not mind.

Me: That will not be necessary. Thank you, though.

Catty-Corner: You seem to be in a good mood today.

Me: Do I?

Catty-Corner: It seems so to me.

Me: Well, I have had a free day so far, and I am about to drive to my meeting with my psychiatrist, which is the only thing on my schedule for the rest of the day, too. Anyone would be happy with a day like that, I bet.

Catty-Corner: I see.

Me: My medication is close to running out, anyway, so it is all timed perfectly, too.

Catty-Corner: What do you mean?

Me: Well, I mean that my psychiatrist is the person who handles my medication, so it is well-timed that I am already going to see him today.

Catty-Corner: It sounds as if it will be well-timed for him, too.

Me: What do you mean?

Catty-Corner: Well, *any* visit of yours could, I suppose, be called well-timed for him since pay must always be well-timed for any professional. Your psychiatrist does, after all, eat upon your issues, so it may even be that he has had to train himself to not salivate at your sight because of the—

Me: I know that you do not know what you are talking about, so I will try to forget it. If you had any idea of what I went through then you would not say things like that.

Catty-Corner: […]

Me: No one should have to go through what I go through.

Catty-Corner: What do you mean?

Me: Well, I have been told that the depression that I suffer from is particularly acute. It was something that my last psychiatrist told me, too, so you cannot say that it is merely a misdiagnosis from this one. There are many people, I bet, who would not be able to keep fighting in the way that I have. Both psychiatrists, in fact, have told me that very thing.

Catty-Corner: You are depressed?

Me: Of course. That is why I am prescribed antidepressants. I am not just depressed, though, but particularly depressed.

Catty-Corner: Do the antidepressants make you happy?

Me: They make me undepressed.

Catty-Corner: I see.

Me: Well, it is obvious that you do not, and it is also obvious that you have no intention of ever doing so. Any psychiatrist would be able to—

Catty-Corner: Are you going to eventually die?

Me: […]

Catty-Corner: Are you going to eventually—

Me: I heard your question, but I am not going to answer it. You are just trying to get into—

Catty-Corner: I am only trying to figure out the nature of your depression. I am depressed, too, after all, so I want to know if—

Me: You are depressed?

Catty-Corner: Of course.

Me: Would you like the phone number of my psychiatrist? I know that he has openings in his schedule, and I will get a referral discount for bringing you in, too.

Catty-Corner: It is too late for me, I think. I am already far too invested in the natural to try to start over elsewhere.

Me: What do you mean?

Catty-Corner: Well, I mean that the unnatural is a place where I am unwilling to go. It is, after all, a whole new realm where I would have to learn all the new—

Me: You are looking at it wrong. Depression is unnatural, not natural, which is something that anyone who has ever felt it knows. After all, depression is what keeps people from feeling like they can live a natural life.

Catty-Corner: Well, are you going to eventually die? How can you call depression unnatural when death is the most natural thing of all?

Me: I already told you that I will not answer your stupid—

Catty-Corner: My point is that if death is natural then depression must be, too. After all, death is life's only universal commonality, which means that it is also the most uniting of experiences, and it is important to remember that our greatest claim to community is our shared doom.

Me: [...]

Catty-Corner: [...]

Me: Well, it is obvious that you are only trying to make me more depressed, which my psychiatrist told me is a defense mechanism used by those who are too scared to admit that they—

Catty-Corner: The truth is that an antidepressant life has no more in common with a *natural* life than a fluorescent room does with a sunny day. The former are but shades of the latter, and they are the retreats of those who cannot face their own existences. You may be able to so singe yourself that you never again feel depression, but you do not get to drag the natural down to those depths with you. One's lack of depression is indicative of one's lack of proper life, and the undepressed life is, in fact, one of the most unnatural of lives that has ever been conceived.

Me: I would be interested to know what a psychiatrist would say about you.

Catty-Corner: Well, what about yourself?

Me: I stopped listening when I could tell what you were going to say.

Caty-Corner: I see.

Me: […]

Catty-Corner: […]

Me: I may mention you to my psychiatrist today. I never have done so before since I know that it would be a waste of time, but the two of us may need a laugh.

Catty-Corner: What will the two of you laugh about?

Me: Well, we will obviously laugh about how stupid you are. We have always had—

Catty-Corner: Will you tell me why I am stupid before you go?

Me: I already did that, and I will not do it again. I will not let you make me late again, either.

Catty-Corner: I see. Well, I await your counterargument. Your psychiatrist can perhaps prescribe one for you.

Me: You obviously do not even know what a psychiatrist is.

ON AGES

Me: Morning, neighbor.

My Catty-Corner Neighbor: Good morning. Are you in a hurry?

Me: Is it that obvious? I am off to the store, and I want to be there as soon as it opens.

Catty-Corner: Is there something that they are running out of?

Me: It is nothing like that. I have an order that was shipped there for me to pick up.

Catty-Corner: Are they offering it to someone else?

Me: Of course not. I want it as soon as possible, though, so that is why I am going now.

Catty-Corner: What is it?

Me: A new television.

Catty-Corner: That does not sound very special. You already have a couple, I think.

Me: This one is new, though, and it has new features. It is able to watch three-dimensional movies, in fact. I am going to need to have them at the store show me how it works, but I know that it has the feature. Can you even imagine what watching a three-dimensional television is going to look like? Things are going to actually look real, I bet.

Catty-Corner: Well, reality and television have always gone together well.

Me: What an age we live in!

Catty-Corner: […]

Me: I did not hear you.

Catty-Corner: I did not say anything.

Me: I obviously know that. You are supposed to say that you agree with me. It is basic common courtesy, after all. When someone marvels at our time then the other person is supposed to do the same after. You are, in fact, supposed to try to outdo me.

Catty-Corner: What an *age* we *live* in!

Me: Why did you say it like that?

Catty-Corner: I repeated what you said. Are your words not able to stand up to repetition?

Me: Do not start trying to twist things like that. You always try to take the simplest thing from me and turn it into something stupid.

Catty-Corner: How was it that I repeated you wrong?

Me: You know what you did.

Catty-Corner: Are you able to tell me?

Me: You said it like it is a bad thing. The way that you said it was mocking, and I will not—

Catty-Corner: That is actually the very thing that I was about to accuse you of.

Me: What do you mean?

Catty-Corner: Your original statement was said in such a mocking way that it was insulting.

Me: That does not make any sense at all. I remember what I said exactly, and I said it with nothing but pride. It was you who made an insult, and it was obvious that you were trying to direct something at me.

Catty-Corner: Is a personal insult the only kind?

Me: What do you mean?

Catty-Corner: Well, what I said may have been an insult to you, but what you said was an insult to everyone everywhere and forever. It is obvious that—

Me: What is actually obvious is that this is just another day when you tried to plan some big thing to be cruel, and it is also obvious that it is just another day when you do not have any point to make at all. All you ever do is try to snap shut the jaws of whatever trap you have laid out for me, so I think that I am going—

Catty-Corner: My point is that we are in a Dark Age. Each of us was born into and will die within it.

Me: That is the stupidest thing that I have ever heard.

Catty-Corner: What do you mean?

Me: It is not me who has anything that needs to be explained. You are the stupid one here, not me, and I should not even be standing here and encouraging you.

Catty-Corner: I will support my claim after you support your assertion that it is stupid. You should not require anything else from me to do so, after all, since you already know enough of my claim to name its stupidity.

Me: You are *still* not making any sense. Your argument is so weak that your explanation of why you do not make sense does not even make sense. It is the same with you every single day, and it is because of the fact that you only ever think about yourself, and you take advantage of every instinct that I have to—

Catty-Corner: Why is what I said stupid?

Me: Because it does not make any sense at all. That is what I have been telling you. You are the only person who would ever be stupid enough to make this argument, too, so that is another way that I am able to know. You can spend your whole, dumb life doing—

Catty-Corner: Why is what I said stupid?

Me: It makes you stupider every time that you ask that. After all, do you really need to have someone point out each and every thing for you that we have done? How about the fact that every great band to ever exist has done so within this supposed *Dark Age* that you have made up and are trying to lie to me about? It does not matter what genre that you think is best because they have all occurred within this timeframe that you are calling worthless. It is so obvious that you are wrong that it is pathetic that I have to correct you, and I am embarrassed by how little you know about the world. How about another example of movies? Every single one of them—

Catty-Corner: A Dark Age is not determined by presence or absence but rather by direction or misguidedness. It would, after all, be stupid to suggest that a claim of a Dark Age was in any way a claim of absence since that would mean regarding nature as an active and attentive player in the whole thing, and it would imply that a Dark Age occurs because nature in some way decides to withhold certain minds who would otherwise have given credence to their time. Simply pointing to the presence of a pile of things that you like, therefore, is not a valid refutation of our Dark Age since that is not at all what the term means. Think of the Roman Dark Age, for example. It did not happen because its well of people dried up but rather because the water in that well was stagnant for so long that it became polluted. Those of that time did not do nothing with their whole lives, after all, but, instead, what they did were things that those who came after them did not care about. *That* is the difference, and it is a very important distinction. A Dark Age occurs whenever the majority of minds spend their lives wasted in some channel rather than continuing up the river. It does not refer to a declining *number* of minds but rather to a declining *state* of those minds. It refers to minds that were never quite able to get out of their own minds, and it refers—

Me: This is stupid, and I am leaving. I am sure that you will be glad to hear that you have ruined my morning, but once I get back from the store with my new television then I can promise that I will forget about you entirely. You can insult me as much as you want and even every single day, which is what you seem to have decided to do with your life, but the best that you will ever be able to do is momentarily upset me. I am above all your attacks, and I look down on them from my—

Catty-Corner: It is important to remember that people always retreat within themselves whenever the world becomes shroudy and unclear, and this is a truth that will always be true. Think, for example, of a neighborhood park. When the sun is out then the park is full of life, but at night the place largely empties, and we come up with scary stories about those who stay within. When the world loses its obvious light then people will always retreat within themselves while coming up with rationalizations for why they are doing so toward what is the *true* light. That is the last point that I want to make. When a political order that long bedrocked all else vanished then Saint Augustine directed the world inward, and the Roman Dark Age ensued. When a religion that long bedrocked all else vanished then Mass Advertising directed the world inward, and the American Dark Age ensued.

Me: I am glad that that was your last point because I would not have given you time for anything else. You cannot say that I did not hear you out, so maybe you will finally be forced to realize that you have to make your arguments make sense before trying to convince people of them. In fact, it does not even matter to you whether I actually believe you, I bet. All you probably want is for me to accept your opinion without debate so that you can persist in it while telling yourself that it is unquestioned. You want to live the unexamined as well as the unchallenged life, which is so obvious to everyone that—

Catty-Corner: Are you going to go to the store?

Me: Of course. I am going now. I do not even know why I wasted any time at all talking to you when I have had a television waiting for me the whole time. In fact, you are the one between the two of us who does not even have a single television in his home, so if anyone could be said to be living in a *Dark* Age then—

Catty-Corner: You should hurry to the store. Every minute that you waste here is, after all, a minute of lost programming there, and when you consider how many channels there are that—

Me: I am going right now. I hope that I will not find you out front when I get back, but you will not be able to upset me, anyway, which is what I already told you, but I know that you will forget it by the time that I get back.

ON TEENAGERS

Me: Afternoon, neighbor.

My Catty-Corner Neighbor: Good afternoon. Are you just waking up? You look rather tired.

Me: I am. I had one of those nights that everyone needs once in a while, even if it means losing a morning.

Catty-Corner: How many friends did you have over?

Me: It was not one of those nights. It was a night just for myself.

Catty-Corner: What do you mean?

Me: Well, a new videogame just came out that is part of a series going back to when I was a kid, so I played that. I do not play videogames much anymore, of course, but it is nice to have a chance to be able to feel like a kid again.

Catty-Corner: What is the game?

Me: I doubt that you have heard of it.

Catty-Corner: What is it about?

Me: Well, it follows and continues the story from the last game. It is mainly about killing aliens, so there is not a whole lot of plot. One of my earliest memories is of playing the first game in the series back when I was a little kid.

Catty-Corner: Would you recommend it? I have a nephew who plays videogames, so he may be interested in it.

Me: How old is he?

Catty-Corner: He is fifteen. His sixteenth birthday is in a month, though.

Me: Well, he will not be able to buy it himself, so you would have to take that into consideration.

Catty-Corner: What do you mean?

Me: I mean that he is not old enough.

Catty-Corner: I have seen him successfully work the controller numerous times.

Me: I mean that he is not old enough to go into a store and buy it for himself. The game is about killing aliens, after all, so it is extremely violent.

Catty-Corner: I see. Well, I do not want to take a chance of making my nephew more violent, so it might be best—

Me: That is easily the stupidest thing that you have said today, and it may be the stupidest thing that you have ever suggested. Everyone knows that violent videogames do not make people more violent.

Catty-Corner: I did not know that. I thought that videogames were considered to be art?

Me: Well, they are. The only people who think otherwise are those who have never played them.

Catty-Corner: Does that mean that videogames are capable of things like deeper messages and examinations of the human condition?

Me: Of course.

Catty-Corner: Do those messages and examinations never take the form of negative things like desensitization to violence?

Me: I already told you that videogames do not do that. The only reason why people say that they do is because they want to hurt the industry.

Catty-Corner: I see.

Me: They do not like videogames, so they make up lies about them. The truth is not as important to them as the furtherance of their side, which they claim to be just another name for the truth.

Catty-Corner: Does that mean that videogames are capable of making a person more of something but only ever in a positive way?

Me: They do not make a person more violent. I can tell you *that* for sure.

Catty-Corner: Well, *that* is rather lucky for the industry. After all, no other *artists* have ever had such a blissful position of making an impact that cannot, by rule, be negative. To know one's message to be both worthwhile and unpervertable is both an artist's dream and heaven. One can only hope that videogame *artists* resolve to only ever use their good powers for good and that the millions whom they dynamically alter continue to be—

Me: None of this is important at all. All I was trying to do was broaden your horizons by telling you about a new piece of art, but I should have known that you would just use the opportunity to ramble pointlessly, which is what you always—

Catty-Corner: My point is that if videogames are capable of deeper messages then it seems obvious that those deeper messages would have the same potentials and pitfalls of all deeper messages. The truth is that you elevate videogames to art whenever such suits you, and you degrade them to entertainment in the same way. If you need to attack then they are art, and if you need to defend then they are entertainment. You do not like

81

having to defend a thing that you like, and your preference thus becomes its best defense. How *could* it ever be negative, after all, when you like it so much? If it makes you feel good then why should you have to justify it? Why would you ever want to take the time to properly defend videogames, after all, when such is necessarily time not spent playing them? Any amount of time removed from pleasure is obviously wasted time, and the only—

Me: If you do not want to hear about the game then I am going to go. I should be getting back, anyway, in fact.

Catty-Corner: I was only interested in whether my nephew would like it. If it is something that he is not legally allowed to be then I would, of course, never allow him to be it.

Me: He will just have to wait until he is older, I suppose. It is a videogame worth waiting for, though, so he will, at the very least, have it to look forward to.

Catty-Corner: How old will he need to be before he can play it?

Me: Well, he will have to wait a while. The earlier videogames in the series are not as violent, so he could start with those, I suppose. They have been making the series more realistic with each new videogame, and it is only with this most recent one that it has become so realistic that it is rated *Adults Only*. The first one, which was probably my favorite, was—

Catty-Corner: Does an *Adults Only* rating mean that the game can only be played by adults?

Me: Of course.

Catty-Corner: Well, why would they do that? Do they not want their game to be played?

Me: If you are trying to say that only kids play videogames then I will not let your insult hurt me. All it does is show how judgmental you are, and it proves that you are too stupid to even be able to—

Catty-Corner: I mean that there are no longer any *adults* at all. Catering to adults in the modern world is like doing the same for corpses.

Me: What do you mean?

Catty-Corner: Well, the old progression went from child to adult, and the new one goes from child to teenager. We have stunted ourselves to prolong both our enjoyment and lack of responsibilities, which are two things that often entwine. It may be true that the creation of the teenager can be dated to the first half of the twentieth century, but the latter half of that century will be remembered for the mindset's triumph and eventual monopolization of the market. There was, after all, a stupid and—

Me: You are not making any sense at all, and it is obvious that you are trying to force an argument into a place where it is not supposed to fit. A teenager is something that everyone who has ever lived has been for a few years, after all, which shows that you—

Catty-Corner: The word *teenager* refers to a mentality, not just an arbitrary range of age. If it only referred to specific years then it could never be defined as having been created, after all.

Me: I think that I am going to go back inside. I was only wanting to come out for a few minutes, anyway. If I am going to spend my time unproductively then I should just play my new videogame since, at the very least, I get enjoyment out of it. There is not a better—

Catty-Corner: The tyranny of the teenager should in no way be surprising since it is, after all, the most gilded of golden means. It is the child who feels no responsibility for the world, it is the adult who feels too much responsibility for it, but it is the teenager who sneers at duty from within its bosom. It is the child who fears the world due to not understanding it, it is the adult who fears the world due to understanding it, but it is the teenager who mocks fear from beside a roaring hearth. It is the child who is scared of not becoming an adult, it is the adult who is scared of never having a child, but it is the teenager who ever revels in the glory of that which he *knows* to be all his own. It is the child who needs a safety net, it is the adult who understands the thing's true impossibility, but it is the teenager who both demands the support's existence as well as its invisibility. It is the child who freely asks to be helped, it is the adult who freely helps, but it is the teenager who justifies an assertion to be helped. It is the child who cannot face the world, it is the adult who realizes that he must face it, but it is the teenager who merely turns himself sideways to better model his form and hide the expressions of his face. It is the child who—

Me: I am leaving. You have not seemed to notice my walking away, so I wanted to let you know. I was going to try to let you finish, but it is obvious that you are only going to keep repeating yourself, so I would rather play my new videogame than subject myself to that sameness.

ON INFORMATION

Me: Morning, neighbor.

My Catty-Corner Neighbor: Good morning. It is good to see you. I am more inclined to call it the afternoon, though.

Me: It is true that I slept in a little later than usual today, I suppose.

Catty-Corner: Did you have a late night?

Me: I was not thinking so at the time. I got caught up in a movie, though, and I got lost in it.

Catty-Corner: What was the movie?

Me: It was a history documentary, and it was one that I would highly recommend. It was extremely entertaining.

Catty-Corner: What was it about from history?

Me: Well, it was not about things from forever ago in the past, so if that is what you mean then you are on the wrong track. The documentary was about the historical importance and implications of now.

Catty-Corner: I see. What was it called?

Me: I cannot remember the title. I know that it had *Information Age* in it, though, so that part was easy to not forget.

Catty-Corner: What do you mean?

Me: Well, *Information Age* is the historical term for now. We live during a time when everyone has access to the information about everything, so that is what sets us apart. Not having the access to what we do is one of the main things that made the people of the past so much stupider than us.

Catty-Corner: I did not know that.

Me: The documentary explains it. It is something that we all somewhat know, though, so the documentary was just confirmation.

Catty-Corner: I was not aware that they did not have information in the past. Did the documentary happen to mention the year in which it was invented?

Me: Do not start getting like that. I am just trying to recommend a movie.

Catty-Corner: I do not get the reasoning, though. I understand that we assume that we know more than anyone who came before us, but I cannot figure out why.

Me: Well, are you aware that the years add up? The year 2000 was one higher than 1999, after all. People build upon the people of the past, and then they themselves get built upon.

Catty-Corner: Is it that simple? History is but a hope slope pointing up to now?

Me: Well, if you mean that progress progresses then that is true. I do not, however, understand why you are having so much trouble with this. Anyone else would be able to tell you the same thing that I am.

Catty-Corner: Well, would you say that devolution is possible?

Me: Do you mean whether it is possible for people to go backward?

Catty-Corner: Is it possible for them to go backward, sideways, or in any way other than what is the determined right, proper, and progressive one?

Me: Of course. If everyone decided to go back to living in caves then everyone would be living in caves, after all.

Catty-Corner: How would that be possible, though? If time is progress and progress is time then how could *anything* help from being progressive?

Me: What do you mean?

Catty-Corner: I am asking what you mean.

Me: I am not going to waste any more of my time with this. I should—

Catty-Corner: Will you tell me more about the documentary?

Me: Why do you want me to?

Catty-Corner: I want to hear why it is the *Information Age*.

Me: Why did you say it like that?

Catty-Corner: I just said it like part of my words.

Me: You said it in a mocking way.

Catty-Corner: All I said is that I want to hear about the Information Age.

Me: You said it different again that time.

Catty-Corner: Well, does that mean that you got what you wanted?

Me: It is not important, anyway. Just say whatever it is that you want to say, or I am going to go.

Catty-Corner: The only thing that I want to say is that I do not think that it is the Information Age.

Me: Then what is it?

Catty-Corner: Well, I would probably call it the *Enfo Age*. It is, after all, a time when not only do we condense information as much as possible, but we also warp it. It is the Enfo Age because information is both chopped up and processed, and it is both stunted and scrambled. It is fair to say that the abundance of information is a characteristic of our time, but we are most defined by our rejection of it, which takes the form of our high-nosed assumption of our power over it. It is important to remember that on each of us at all times is a database that would have made any educated mind in any prior age weep with a bliss of such magnitude that such an individual would likely only be able to define the thing as manifested heaven. With all at our fingertips, however, we have forgotten how to perform the very action of a reach, and, instead, we have decided to use the power of being able to look up anything as a way of knowing nothing. The Cult of the Now has given way to the Cult of the Instant, and the further inward the loop goes then the further will it fray further and further layers of what was its nearer and nearer selves. To call our time the *Information Age* would, therefore, be an insult to information. After all, it is not information's fault, and the poor thing continues to try as hard today as it ever has before. *Enfo*, which is a word reduced by a ridiculous percentage as well as idiotically altered, perfectly displays—

Me: I am leaving. If you want then you can continue talking.

Catty-Corner: Are you going somewhere?

Me: I am going back inside.

Catty-Corner: Can we continue this conversation tonight?

Me: I may be able, but I will likely not be, though.

Catty-Corner: How about tomorrow?

Me: I do not think so.

Catty-Corner: Why not?

Me: I am going to be busy.

Catty-Corner: How about another day?

Me: We will see. You really should just watch the documentary, though.

ON IDENTITY

Me: Evening, neighbor.

My Catty-Corner Neighbor: Good evening. I cannot tell whether you seem to be having a good day or a bad one, which usually, I suppose, means that you are having a unique one. In fact, it looks to me as if—

Me: It is a bad day. That is something that I can tell you for sure.

Catty-Corner: Well, there appears to be some smile in that grimace that I see.

Me: I do not need to have you tell me about me. I know myself, after all, so it is unnecessary, and what you said did not make any sense at all, anyway.

Catty-Corner: I see.

Me: If you are actually wanting to ask about my bad day then I will tell you, but I am not in the mood to waste any of my time. I just told you that my day has been bad, and I have, in fact, already had several hours of it wasted.

Catty-Corner: What do you mean?

Me: Well, there is a friend of mine whom I occasionally get together with. We tend to argue, but we have always found ways to remain friends. This civility of ours, however, has started to change, and it has, in fact, become more crumbled than a coastline, and I have to watch as microscopic pieces of it are ceaselessly eaten away. It took me too long to first notice the descent, I think, since its existence burst upon me today, and I do not know if things will ever be the same again. I can only hope so, I suppose, since it is not me who needs to make a change back.

Catty-Corner: What do you mean?

Me: Well, my friend has fallen off politically. There were hypotheticals that we used to discuss that are now his realities and that we must argue about. It does not matter the way in which I try to present a fact to him because he has become convinced that nothing is fact without in some way first being him. He has, in fact, become such a practitioner of identity politics that he cannot—

Catty-Corner: What are *identity politics*?

Me: Do you really not know what they are?

Catty-Corner: I have, I think, heard of them, but I do not, however, know how they differ from politics.

Me: Well, they are a new form of politics, I suppose, but even calling them that is too much, and they are, instead, a new form of *subversion* of politics. Identity politics is the newest way that people have found to tell themselves that they are more important than others and then to act accordingly.

Catty-Corner: Well, they sound like someone whom I know. He is, after all, always—

Me: I know that you are going to try to talk about me, so you can stop now. If anyone is a practitioner of identity politics then it is you, not me. It is, after all, you who is always different and—

Catty-Corner: The truth is that there is no such thing as identity politics. Instead, the term simply refers to the politics of those who already engage in an identity existence. The *identity* of the term is, therefore, unnecessary since there is no other type of politics that such an individual can engage in. After all, his decision that life only goes as far as his own ears *must*, by rule, have been made before his decision to see his country in the same way. Identity politics is but the inevitable extension of the identity existence, which means that if identity politics worry you then you have so far only seen the beast's tail.

Me: [...]

Catty-Corner: [...]

Me: There are many ways that you are worse than my friend. He will, at the very least, listen to me rather than talk his own way into a tangent that does not make any sense at all, anyway. I know that you are just trying to make things sound scary to try to—

Catty-Corner: Concerning yourself with identity politics is like stressing over the blood on the floor while it is still pouring from the vein. After all, if someone practices identity politics then that means that he is *unable* to practice any other, not *unwilling*. It is, in other words, a case of inability rather than intent, and when that rearing head finally—

Me: It is obvious that you are the only one of us who practices identity politics, and it is also obvious that you do not even know what they are, so I am not going to waste any more of my time trying to point out the obvious to you. I was already having a bad day, too, which you obviously did not care about.

ON VICTORS

Me: Morning, neighbor.

My Catty-Corner Neighbor: Good morning. It is good to see you. I have not run into you for the past few days, so I was starting to get worried.

Me: You were, I bet, more excited than worried.

Catty-Corner: What do you mean?

Me: I mean that you had a few days of being the only fish in your puddle, which meant that you were, by rule, the *big fish*. I was, in other words, not around for you to have to duck.

Catty-Corner: Well, if you were avoiding me then that changes things. You do, after all, tend to duck our talks whenever they are just—

Me: That is not true. The only times when I walk away from you are when you give me no choice, which obviously means that they are your own fault. I was on a vacation, anyway, so you are doubly wrong.

Catty-Corner: Where did you go?

Me: I drove to a national park for the weekend. I am sure that I have mentioned to you before that it is something that I have always wanted to do, so I have been looking for my chance. It was not planned at all, but I had a long weekend with a free schedule, so I made the decision to go. I was there for two days and one night.

Catty-Corner: Did you have a good time?

Me: I learned a lot.

Catty-Corner: What do you mean?

Me: Well, I keep my mind open at the same time as my ears, so I acquire knowledge as I go through life, which is a habit that you should try to pick up from me. I learned, for example, about the history of the area, and I learned that it was one of the places where Americans exterminated Native Americans. I was told that it—

Catty-Corner: The Native Americans were exterminated?

Me: Of course not. Americans tried to exterminate them, though, which is what is important.

Catty-Corner: I see.

Me: Well, it is obvious that you do not want to hear about my—

Catty-Corner: The truth is that Native Americans are one of the few native peoples in history to have *not* been wiped out. After all, the sheer fact that we are aware of them is enough to number them among the most fortunate of those whom they are counted among, and their continued existence belies the role that you try to make them play in the same way that your continual ignorance must make of you a liar.

Me: […]

Catty-Corner: […]

Me: Well, history is, I suppose, written by the victor, so I should not be surprised that you have such a—

Catty-Corner: What do you mean?

Me: I mean that the view of history always supports the winning side, which is something that everyone knows, and it is the reason why you are supposed to be skeptical of anything that you read from the past.

Catty-Corner: What about kings?

Me: What do you mean?

Catty-Corner: Well, they are rarely remembered well, and this poor remembrance extended to their own times, too. It is, in fact, the unsuccessful *pretender* to the crown who was most often recalled romantically while the *ruler* was at best tolerated until death could allow for damnation. After all, if victors have been the ones writing history then why have they not been better remembered?

Me: That is not what we are talking about at all, and what you said does not make any sense, anyway, so you should not—

Catty-Corner: My point is that history is rarely among the prizes selected by the victor to be part of his spoils. Why, after all, would a victor ever concern himself with the *past* when in possession of the *present*? The truth is that history is far more often written by the vanquished than it is by those who have vanquished them, and to rule is, in fact, one of the best ways of ensuring that one will not be remembered well.

Me: [...]

Catty-Corner: It is also important to—

Me: I do not want to hear anything else from you that will not make sense. I know that you are probably conservative, anyway, so it was stupid of me to even start—

Catty-Corner: Of course.

Me: [...]

Catty-Corner: [...]

Me: What do you mean?

Catty-Corner: Well, I mean that I am, of course, conservative. Everyone, after—

Me: I have had enough of you for today. I need to finish unpacking, anyway, so I should not—

Catty-Corner: The truth is that everyone is *conservative*, but there are no longer any actual *Conservatives*. There is a difference between the two, and it is a very important distinction. Everyone is conservative in that their doctrine is older than themselves, but there are no more Conservatives in that they have been educated away. After all, generations of the right have now been raised by the left, so true conservatism has become obscured, and its place has been taken by that which is called *anti-liberalism*. The students were only taught one side, so when they rejected it then they could only hate it, and it should, therefore, not be surprising that the battle has gone from that of left with right to that of left with *troll*, which—

Me: I said that I have had enough of you for today

ON TERRORISM

Me: Afternoon, neighbor.

My Catty-Corner Neighbor: Good afternoon. Did something happen?

Me: What do you mean?

Catty-Corner: You do not seem well. I hope that there is not anything wrong.

Me: Well, that is like hoping for there to be nothing at all. Things have become so broken that there is hardly anything left complete without some glaring fault.

Catty-Corner: Is that what is bothering you?

Me: Of course not. I have long ago accepted that.

Catty-Corner: Then what is it?

Me: My neck is strained. It feels like there is a pinch in it that will not go away, and it has been such a long—

Catty-Corner: Your *neck*?

Me: My *neck*.

Catty-Corner: What is it strained from?

Me: That is what I was in the process of telling you before you interrupted me.

Catty-Corner: Well, I needed clarification, and I was not sure if what—

Me: You needed clarification, and it did not bother you in the slightest to upset me to get it. In fact, I bet that the thought did not even cross you mind. I was in the middle of explaining things to you, and you could not even wait for me to finish. You were getting your way, and you *still* could not wait your turn, which just shows how much of a child you are.

Catty-Corner: Well, I suppose that it is true that a question is now often regarded as an interruption, and a blow is the expected return for any blow.

Me: That does not make any sense at all. You are just trying to speak vaguely so that I will not be able to have an answer.

Catty-Corner: Would it be different if I spoke *vividly*?

Me: That would be up to you.

Catty-Corner: What do you mean?

Me: I mean that it would obviously depend on what you said. It is your job to convince me, after all. If I am on one side of an argument and you on the other then it is up to you to bring me over, and if you fail then it is your failure rather than mine. Anyone will tell you that it is not the wrong person's fault if the right person does not do a good enough job of laying out his own argument. These things are obvious to anyone who pays attention, which obviously does not include you.

Catty-Corner: Does that mean that correction is the responsibility of the corrector rather than the one in need of correction?

Me: Of course. If you want someone to change his mind then you have to breach his walls. It is not his duty to leave what he knows and to sally out to meet you on the plain. After all, that would not make any sense because it would mean that the expectation would be for him to be willing to attack himself along with you, which is obviously absurd. People are like castles, and if they are ever wrong then it is the duty of the sieging army to force them out. It is absolutely ridiculous to think of the responsibility being the other way around, and it is also selfish in a way that proves—

Catty-Corner: Will you tell me why your neck is strained?

Me: That is what I have been trying to tell you this whole time, and I would have done it a while ago, too. You are the one who interrupted me, after all, so it is your own fault, and you should learn to have some responsibility for yourself, which is the very—

Catty-Corner: Why is your neck strained?

Me: It is strained due to all the time that I am having to spend looking over my shoulder. It has even reached the point that I feel as if I have to look over the shoulder of my own shoulder-looking.

Catty-Corner: What do you mean?

Me: I mean that there is hardly a single day that goes by without an act of terrorism being committed. If you are actually willing to pay enough attention to the news then you will hear about them. We are being assaulted on all sides by people whose anger at our lives is rivaled only by their jealousy of them. They are always attacking, so we must always remain on guard.

Catty-Corner: Do you mean that there could be a terrorist around every corner?

Me: Of course. You may not always be able to see them because of the ways that they have of hiding, but they are there. Their greatest tactic has always been finding ways to live among us, after all. There are domestic terrorists, too, so you have to be even more careful about—

Catty-Corner: Looking for terrorists around every corner is foolish when they are actually looking down on us from the balconies above. They may have once sat in dim places underground, but they have long since moved overhead, and the lighting on them is so good that they now hire others to manicure their appearances. Terrorism, in other words, was the old game, and it is terror *of* terrorism that is the new one.

Me: It is obvious that you are just trying to scare me so that I will agree with you, but I will not let it work because I will not believe you. I know who terrorists are because I have seen them in the news for years, so I will not let you tell me otherwise. You are just angry at the world, so you are making up villains to try to trick me into—

Catty-Corner: Any making up being done is the work of those villains themselves. It is important to remember that the tactics used by the victorious underdog will *always* be adopted by the next top dog, and this means that any advances made by a rebel father will eventually be used against his subject son. If it worked for you yesterday then it will be employed against you today, and if it is working for you today then it will be hired away tomorrow. Success does, after all, breed success, and this remains true even when that successfulness is monstrous. Terrorism succeeded, and it changed the world, and it is now the turn of terror *of* terrorism, and if the former was decentralized and savage then the latter is centralized and sadistic. It is, after all, a terrorist currently holed up in the Grand Backwater's Great Bunker. It is, after all, a terrorist currently brushing the Dragon's teeth. It is, after all, a terrorist currently belted by the Chain. It is, after all, a terrorist currently atop whatever that thing is that is starving the north half of Korea. It is, after—

Me: If your only purpose is to scare me then I am going to leave. All you are tying to do is make me mistrust those who are actually on my side, but your paranoia will not consume me. I will not let you use fear to destroy my life.

Catty-Corner: Fear destroying one's life is far less terrifying than having it *create* that life. The truth is that fear was formerly used by terrorists to attempt to destroy, but it has been co-opted by creation, and it is in the process of remaking the world in its own image.

Me: Well, it sounds like you have made whatever point that you were wanting to make, so I am going to go back inside.

Catty-Corner: Do you agree with me?

Me: Of course not.

Catty-Corner: How do you know that I am wrong?

Me: Because it is obvious. You can ask anyone, and you will hear the same thing. People are not as weak as you seem to think them to be. If you say things designed to hurt them then they will hurt you back, and—

Catty-Corner: Is this your counterargument?

Me: It is a warning.

Catty-Corner: Well, will you share your counterargument with me? That way, I will be able to choose the right side to be on rather than being eventually forced to take it.

Me: I have already told you that you are wrong, so I will not keep doing it. I am going inside, and I do not care what you do. If you want to persist in your wrongness then I can promise that you will be buried in your coming comeuppance. It would be wise of you to think twice before trying to trick anyone into this argument of yours. I need to go back inside now, anyway. The best thing for my neck is lying down with my eyes closed.

Catty-Corner: I see.

Me: I suppose that you have made me forget about my neck pain for a few minutes, so I can, at the very least, thank you for that.

ON CONSPIRACY

Me: Evening, neighbor.

My Catty-Corner Neighbor: Good evening. Is there something that you are looking for?

Me: What do you mean?

Catty-Corner: Well, you seem to be scrutinizing into the heavens rather than staring. I often look at nothing myself, of course, but I do not do so as intently as you appear to be doing.

Me: I am just looking at the night sky.

Catty-Corner: You are not looking away from it.

Me: Well, I want to make sure that my eyes are in the right place. You saw, I bet, the news reports about the recent UFO sighting. I do not believe in them, of course, but if one does fly by then I want to be sure to see it.

Catty-Corner: [...]

Me: If it does, in fact, come then this is the area where they said that it will likely happen, too. Some of my coworkers said that they were going to do the same thing tonight, so even if nothing happens then we will have that to talk about tomorrow.

Catty-Corner: I see.

Me: The possibility of a UFO sighting terrifies you, I bet. You are scared of there actually being anything out there, so you are one of those who call people conspiracy theorists whenever they are not willing to bury their—

Catty-Corner: The only *conspiracy* that I am afraid of is conspiracy theorists themselves, and they are, in fact, far more terrifying than even the most monstrous of their theories. These are, after all, those who take the worst of their neighbors for *granted*, and they—

Me: You are not making any sense at all. Conspiracy theorists are suspicious about their government, not their neighbors. I am not one, anyway.

Catty-Corner: I see.

Me: I bet that you will only ever see whatever the government wants you to see.

Catty-Corner: The truth is that any conspiracy theory's most convincing element is convenience. Take, for example, the conspiracy theory that the government has been hiding the existence of UFOs. The very age of this conspiracy theory will, in fact, prove my point, and the only thing required is for one to acknowledge the fact that it extends further back than one generation.

Me: [...]

Catty-Corner: Will you acknowledge that fact?

Me: It does not seem important, so I do not see why it should matter.

Catty-Corner: Well, whether it matters is something that we can test rather than term, which means that we—

Me: That does not make any sense at all, and this is all obviously just another of your attempts to make me seem stupid by acting that way yourself, and you want me to look like—

Catty-Corner: My point is that the conspiracy theory's longevity is itself proof against its actual existence. After all, the government agents who supposedly hide aliens today are those who were children interested in uncovering them yesterday, and the conspiracy theorist, therefore, must be willing to believe that all who are skeptical like him are also willing to sell themselves unlike him. A conspiracy theorist *must*, by rule, regard himself as especial, and he *must* regard the world as but the weak and himself. Everyone except himself is suspect in his mind, and there is not—

Me: You are not describing conspiracy theorists at all. I have already told you that they are those who are suspicious about their government, not their neighbors. They are the watchdogs of society, and they remain skeptical where everyone else—

Catty-Corner: They may have once been *skeptical*, but they have slid into an assumption of the sinister. There is a difference between the two, and it is a very important distinction. Conspiracy theorists do not, for example, prove to you why the astronauts of the eleventh Apollo were willing frauds, but, instead, they *assume* such. Their accusations do not make sense without the assumptions, so they make them without the slightest concern for the harm that they do, and they do, in fact, congratulate themselves on their being so aloof and eroding. It is important to remember that the very consideration of a conspiracy theory requires this assumption of the sinister, and the truth is that your belief in the monster next door will itself be both the match and fuel of such eventually becoming so. In other words, one will—

Me: I do not need to listen to any more of this when I have other things to do. I can go look for the UFO in my backyard, after all, and I may not have as good of a view, but I will, at the very least, be away from you. I already told you that I am not a conspiracy theorist, anyway, so it is obvious that you were not listening to me.

ON SYSTEMIC

Me: Afternoon, neighbor.

My Catty-Corner Neighbor: Good afternoon. It is good to see you. You look like you are having a nice day.

Me: I am, and I hope that you are having a nice one, too.

Catty-Corner: I am so far, I suppose, but there is, however, one—

Me: It is this being so close to the end of the year that is so nice, I think. We will soon be done with this dreadful year, and it will be put into the past forever, so that fact alone is worth smiling about. Everything, I bet, will be better and back to normal once we change to the new calendar.

Catty-Corner: [...]

Me: I am, in fact, more hopeful for the new year than others are, too. I have always been that way.

Catty-Corner: [...]

Me: There are, of course, a lot of things that I am hopeful for, but there is one that I place higher than the others, and it is that I am hopeful that we can finally reach a time when there is no longer so much systemic abuse plaguing the system. If not in this year then in the next. After all, I am—

Catty-Corner: Can you define that word for me?

Me: Which word?

Catty-Corner: Well, if we had the time then it would likely be enlightening to go through each of them. I am, however, asking about *systemic* since you did not—

Me: Why is that something that you need to ask?

Catty-Corner: Because I want to know.

Me: All you have to do is to watch the news to know what I am talking about. It is what everyone else is willing to do, after all, so I would not have this problem if I were talking to—

Catty-Corner: Well, the word must still have a definition beyond its pointed description, and there must—

Me: *Systemic* refers to whenever people plan on putting into place something that is designed to—

Catty-Corner: What you are beginning to describe is the *systematic*, not the *systemic*. There is a difference between the two, and it is a very important distinction. The first, after all, is nothing more than—

Me: The problems that I am talking about are ones that everyone knows, so they do not need to be forced into your definitions. I am hopeful for them to end, too, so it is obvious that I am thinking about them in the right way.

Catty-Corner: I see.

Me: I know things when I see them, too, so I do not need to waste time with you like this. I am going to go continue my nice day somewhere far—

Catty-Corner: The truth is that the things most often abused as *systemic* are, instead, instances of the *systematic*, which are themselves instances of the system itself being abused. To blame the system for the abuse that it suffers is, therefore, misguided, and it is an example of blaming the victim. After all, the most glaring fault in the American system is Americans, and systematic abuse of the system is, in fact, the most systemic aspect of our society.

Me: I am having such a nice day that I did not interrupt you, but if you are done then I will be gone. It is obvious that you are just trying to upset me over something that does not make any sense, anyway, so I will not—

Catty-Corner: My point is that abuse of the system is in no way an indictment of the system. It is important to remember that the fact that power corrupts says a lot more about people than it does about power, and it is also important to remember that the complete rejection of a system is the same as an unconditional surrender to it. To decry all is to soon be left unable to decry at all, and if all is termed *bad* then the very definition of the word will eventually become muddled then lost, and when such occurs then the world will be in a state too monstrous for us to even now conceive.

Me: I let you finish again, so you cannot say that I did not give you every opportunity to make sense today. It is, in fact, obvious that I did everything that I could.

ON IMMIGRATION

Me: Afternoon, neighbor.

My Catty-Corner Neighbor: Good afternoon. It is good to see you.

Me: Are you just getting home from work?

Catty-Corner: I am. How was your day?

Me: It was good enough, I suppose. It sure was a hot one, though.

Catty-Corner: You will not hear any argument from me on that. I got so many news notifications all day that I was hardly able to keep up.

Me: What do you mean?

Catty-Corner: Well, the country is on fire. That is what I mean.

Me: I meant the weather.

Catty-Corner: […]

Me: What was this news that you think is so important?

Catty-Corner: Do you really not even know?

Me: Well, will you tell me? You only know because you heard it from elsewhere, after all, and it was not even from someone you know, I bet. How do you know that whatever it happens to be is even true?

Catty-Corner: You do not even know what it is, and you are already ready to call it fake. If it did not pass before your own—

Me: I am, at the very least, not stupid enough to just eat up whatever agrees with me.

Catty-Corner: Do you want to know the news or not?

Me: Go ahead and tell me.

Catty-Corner: Another batch of Americans was rounded up and deported today.

Me: […]

Catty-Corner: That does not bother you?

Me: Well, who were they?

Catty-Corner: Does it matter?

Me: Of course.

Catty-Corner: Is that really an answer that you should be able to give without thinking about it? What you want is to find out if you know them or if they matter to you, and then you will decide whether to be outraged.

Me: Well, tell me who they are.

Catty-Corner: They were just another group of Americans accused of having entered the country illegally.

Me: Well, did they?

Catty-Corner: What do you mean?

Me: Were they illegal immigrants?

Catty-Corner: What is an *illegal immigrant*?

Me: It is someone who comes into the country illegally. Are you really too stupid to know that?

Catty-Corner: Are you really too stupid to think about it? Prove to me that it is possible to come to this country illegally, and I will agree with you that we should fix bayonets and force out anyone who does not meet our standard.

Me: Well, the government obviously has to have some way to control things at the border, and there is not—

Catty-Corner: Do you mean the federal government?

Me: Of course.

Catty-Corner: Why is its involvement something that is obvious? Have you not read your Constitution lately?

Me: What do you mean?

Catty-Corner: Congress as originally conceived and prior to themselves changing the spirit had no right to determine who came into this country or in what numbers. It is right there in Article 1, in fact. One is the number before two, which you may not be aware of since you—

Me: I do not care about originally conceived or any other stupid arguments like that. I can count to the number *now*, and that is what I am talking about. We are talking about now, not back then.

Catty-Corner: Does that mean that ideals are supposed to be the first changes of the tough when things get going so? What is precedent, after all, but a nine-letter word that fits under one's shoe?

Me: Well, what is it that you want? Do you think that we should just ignore our borders and let whatever happens happen? Your brain is so waterlogged from your stupid, bleeding heart that you do not care about anything else.

Catty-Corner: If you want to line up the army along every border that our country has then go ahead. It would be, after all, pay for one's neighbors. Would you agree, however, that any Americans would be allowed to cross the lines into their own country?

Me: Of course. The people who they would be there to stop are illegal immigrants.

Catty-Corner: What is an *illegal immigrant*?

Me: I already told you that. Have you not been listening to me? Get your ears out of your own head.

Catty-Corner: Get your mind out of yours. Give me a plain definition of an illegal immigrant. That way, I will be able to identify them as easily as you do.

Me: That will, in fact, be easy. An illegal immigrant is someone who was not born here, does not have American parents, or who does not apply for citizenship in the proper way.

Catty-Corner: What do you mean by the *proper* way?

Me: Well, there are citizenship tests and all sorts of other steps. There are quotas, too, I think.

Catty-Corner: Does that mean that someone who was not born in the United States, who does not have American parents, and who does not take a citizenship test is, by rule, an illegal immigrant?

Me: Of course.

Catty-Corner: Was General Washington an illegal immigrant? Not born in the United States, not having American parents, and never taking a citizenship or any other qualifying test then should he be declared as such?

Me: You are twisting words.

Catty-Corner: You are twisting yourself so as to avoid them. Answer my question.

Me: It is an easy question to answer. Do you actually think that your blind revisionism can affect me? General Washington was a citizen of Virginia. Have you heard of it? It is a state. General Washington did not need to have been born in the United States, he did not need American parents, and he did not need to take any test because Virginia was an immediate part of the United States as soon as it was declared.

Catty-Corner: Does that mean that on July 4th, 1776 every citizen of Virginia became an immediate citizen of the United States?

Me: Of course.

Catty-Corner: Be careful to not let your revisionism show. After all, have you ever heard of the Loyalists?

Me: Why do they matter?

Catty-Corner: Well, have you heard of the Treaty of Paris? Because the two sides who fought in the War of Independence did not share your idea at all, and it is right there in the document. The treaty states that both sides acknowledged the fact that there remained *real British subjects* within the United States at the war's end. As late as the document's signing in 1783, therefore, not everyone who was or had been in the United States was regarded by the two countries as an American. If what you said about General Washington becoming an automatic citizen at the time of the Declaration is true then how could it be that others who were in the same situation did not have the same outcome?

Me: Well, because the Loyalists did not want to be Americans.

Catty-Corner: That is, in fact, the complete truth. A *decision* is the only threshold for citizenship. General Washington may have been a natural-born citizen by way of his birth in Virginia, but he was first a citizen by way of his actions and his willingness to be. The term *illegal immigration* is thus a misnomer because it is impossible to come to the country illegally. General Washington and the fellow Americans in his army prove that American citizenship from its very beginning was not based on place of birth, or one's parents, or one's physical location, or one's score on some test. General Washington made what amounted to an immediate immigration by way of his actions upon at once being able to do so by the United States' founding in the same way that any immigrant has immediate claim to do the same in the years following. The very act of openly desiring to be an American is the legal basis for being one. As long as the United States exists then anyone, anywhere, and at any time has a legal claim to being an American, and demanding otherwise is as repugnant as it is unreasonable. It will always be seen that—

Me: I should head inside. It is getting late, and it is just about time for dinner.

Catty-Corner: Are you sure? I was almost done with my point, and then I was looking forward to hearing your counterargument.

Me: We have been out here for a while.

Catty-Corner: Well, will you share your counterargument before going in? That way, I will know it, and I will be able to think about it.

Me: There really is not time. I am so hungry that I am practically starving.

Catty-Corner: I see. Well, I await your counterargument. Will you have time after dinner?

Me: We have already spent a lot of time arguing about it today.

Catty-Corner: Are you available tomorrow or the next day?

Me: We will have to see.

ON FIRSTNESS

Me: Afternoon, neighbor.

My Catty-Corner Neighbor: [...]

Me: Are you okay over there?

Catty-Corner: I am. I apologize. I was lost in thought. There is a problem that I have been struggling with for years, but I can never seem to make it make any sense. It returns to me at certain times.

Me: What is the problem?

Catty-Corner: Well, I have never been able to understand why everyone is so anti-Vietnam. I have had a lot of time to think about it, of course, but that has not helped at all. One would usually expect the opinions of the past to become clearer the further that they are removed from us, but we are far beyond that sort of normalcy, I suppose.

Me: I know that you are lying, so you can stop the act. You are just trying to make some stupid point that will not make any sense, anyway, I bet. Everyone knows that Vietnam is one of the biggest stains in the history of the world.

Catty-Corner: Well, that may be true, but they still exist. They feel pain in the same way that we do, after all, and it may be that they have aspirations for life in a manner similar to us, and those aspirations could even be very similar to our own. Just because it may not feel good to have to think about them does not mean that they do not—

Me: The only person whom you are describing is yourself, and it does not surprise me at all to hear you try to use the conditions of those people for your own purposes. You are not making any sense at all, anyway, which is what I just said would happen.

Catty-Corner: My point is that I am not sure what the Vietnamese did to earn our scorn. We seem to like their food and their tourist destinations, after all, so I am not sure what we should have against them. Maybe it is as simple as the fact that thinking of them means that, by rule, we must think of ourselves slightly less.

Me: The anti-Vietnam movement was against the Vietnam *War*, not the Vietnamese. What was against the Vietnamese was the war, and everyone knows that it was only fought to try to take over the country.

Catty-Corner: Are you referring to the South Vietnamese?

Me: What do you mean?

Catty-Corner: Are the South Vietnamese the ones whom you are talking about as having imperial ambitions over Vietnam? The war was between them and North Vietnam, after all, with the United States, China, and the Soviet Union added in.

Me: None of this is important, anyway. The Vietnam War was one of the worst things to ever happen. You can ask anyone, and you will hear the same thing. Have you not seen footage of it?

Catty-Corner: Are you able to tell me what was wrong with the war?

Me: That is what I have been doing this whole time. It is something that is easy to do, too, since it is something that everyone knows. The Vietnam War was a *war*, after all, which means that it cannot have been good. You do not even have to know history to know that the United States is the most warmongering great power of all time, and it is obviously—

Catty-Corner: The reason why you believe that about the United States is because you lost the war for your own mind a long time ago. Name for me—

Me: The only reason that you say that is because you do not have an actual answer for me. I am always careful to make sure that the things that I say are those that I have heard others say before, but you only care about yourself, and you try to—

Catty-Corner: Name for me the *least* warmongering great power of all time.

Me: What do you mean?

Catty-Corner: Well, if the United States is the most then what is the least?

Me: That is not what we are talking about at all. You are just trying to excuse the behavior of the United States by finding examples that are not important. If you never learn how to shine the light of criticism upon yourself then you will always continue to—

Catty-Corner: The truth is that the United States is the least warmongering great power of all time, and this fact is so historically incontestable that entertaining the other side is evidence of an utter lack of knowledge. It is important to remember that a thing cannot be the worst of something unless you are able to first determine other things that are less bad than it. It is easy, after all, to call something the *most* when you do not take the time to determine the *least*, and it becomes even easier when you ignore the scale altogether.

Me: It does not surprise me at all to hear this from you. I have, after all, never known a more American-centric American in my entire—

Catty-Corner: Is it not odd that those who decry American centrism are those most unable to speak of elsewhere? Anything, after all, can be *centric* when it is

128

your only example, and the most monolingual and historically illiterate of American generations has found a way to sneer at those who would be appalled by the very sight of them. The truth is that their issue is with American *exceptionalism*, not centrism. These are people who only want to live, after all, and American exceptionalism forces the existence of a bar above their heads. The reminder that there is a baseline that they should be living up to is the most acute of injustices to them, and all they want to do is to pile up as much as they can into their own lives without anyone pointing out—

Me: I am going to go back inside. You obviously just want to try to attack me and make me seem—

Catty-Corner: Will you tell me what the Vietnam War protestors were protesting before you go?

Me: I have already done that. Everyone knows what they were protesting, and it is right there in their name, too, so you do not even have to think about it. They were protesting both the Vietnam War and all wars, which—

Catty-Corner: That is not true. It is impossible that those who protested the Vietnam War were protesting wars.

Me: What do you mean?

Catty-Corner: Well, if they were so against war then where were the calls to lawfully return the country to the oversight of the British, and why was there no one saying that slaves should be returned to their chains? If all wars are bad and unnecessary then the products of all wars *must*, by rule, be bad and not necessary. In fact, one could say that the protestors' very act of massing in protest was itself an endorsement of war since a war had been required to win for them that right to protest. The truth is that they were not against war but rather against *their* involvement in war. There is a difference between the two, and it is a very important distinction. It was their belief, I suppose, that if others of the world *actually* desired self-government then they would have had the foresight to be born within a country practicing it, and *ally* was to them nothing more than another of those four-letter words that had to be banished so that—

Me: It is good to know that you are such a friend of death. There is not a single—

Catty-Corner: It is sad to see that you have wallowed into such an enemy of life. You have—

Me: That does not make any sense at all, and it is not true, anyway. Everyone knows that Vietnam War protestors were heroes, and there is not—

Catty-Corner: Well, they were heroes to themselves, I suppose. Their actions greatly benefited their own personal lives, so if that is heroism then they are some of the greatest heroes that the world has ever seen. The truth, however, is that their ancestors had won for them that which they wanted, and the idea of doing the same for others crossed their minds only as an option to be crossed off. Those whose rights had been gained by revolution and furthered by civil war came to the conclusion that they already had what *they* wanted, so what more could be needed? You have said that American centrism is deplorable in its narrowness, but is self-centrism not an even thinner chute? It is a further degree removed, after all. How does that phrase of ours go? *Our death is a tragedy, but another's is a statistic.* Is that it?

Me: I know what you are trying to do, and it will not work. You want to make Vietnam protestors out as selfish people when they were actually the most altruistic of all peoples, which is something that everyone knows. They were not the ones saying things like *America first*, after all, and they—

Catty-Corner: The reason why such issue is taken with the idea of *America first* is because those who do so regard that spot as reserved for themselves. After all, could there be anything actually more *America first* than the assertion that an ally's life is worth less than one's own? Is a philosophy of *America first* actually any more selfish than that of *Americans first*? The truth is that there may be those who champion the idea of

America first to the letter, but we have all long practiced it in spirt. Having gotten ours—

Me: I am going inside. It sounds like there is a lot more that you have to say, so I do not want to be in your way since you would only—

Catty-Corner: It is important to remember that assertions make asses just as often as assumptions do. Those who protested the Vietnam War were protesting the idea that others and their experiences have the same validity as their own. They did not view the unfortunate of the world as those who happened to be unlucky and who were in need of help, but, instead, they viewed themselves as the lucky of the world and who were in need of conservation. There is every day an inquisitive mind being snuffed out by its situation in the world, but we have decided that it is too much trouble to have to be inquisitive about it. After all, why should another couple lost generations matter when it occurs to those whom we do not care about? Saving lives takes time out of—

Me: I am closing the door now. If you want then you can keep talking, but there is no reason to keep directing yourself to me.

ON IMPORTANCE

Me: Afternoon, neighbor.

My Catty-Corner Neighbor: Good afternoon. I did not expect to see you until this evening. Are you feeling sick?

Me: Well, I am not feeling well. I was having a normal morning, but then things changed, and I began to feel as if I needed to run out of the place. We all know what this feeling feels like, though it is impossible to describe, and everyone knows the best remedy for it, too. It is, therefore, only a little self-care that I am in need of, and my boss understood. I will, I bet, be fine by this evening.

Catty-Corner: […]

Me: Are you actually going to act like you do not know what I am talking about? Everyone has times when taking care of oneself is necessary, so I will not let you make me feel bad about having them myself. It is the most important thing that you can do, after all, and there is—

Catty-Corner: Taking care of oneself is the most important thing that one can do?

Me: Of course. That is what I just said, and everyone knows—

Catty-Corner: The *most* important?

Me: What do you mean?

Catty-Corner: Well, what about, for example, the care of two others? If taking care of *one's* own person is that which has importance then does taking care of *two* people, by rule, not have to be more—

Me: That is not what we are talking about at all. We are talking about self-care, not anything to do with others. You have to take care of yourself before being able to take care of someone else, anyway, which is something that everyone knows, so what you said did not make any sense at all.

Catty-Corner: What about conflicts between these *most* importants?

Me: What do you mean?

Catty-Corner: Well, take a police officer, for example. If there was an intruder in your home then you would, I bet, call the police, and you would, I bet, expect the arrival of an officer.

Me: Of course. That is the purpose of the police.

Catty-Corner: Would you expect him to come inside upon arrival?

Me: Of course. That is where the intruder is, after all.

Catty-Corner: If confronted then is it possible that the intruder might harm the officer rather than you?

Me: Of course. Officers are supposed to announce themselves, too, so that the intruder becomes distracted from me.

Catty-Corner: Well, if his thing of *most* importance might be threated then why would the officer actually do any of these things?

Me: Because it is his job.

Catty-Corner: I see.

Me: Well, it is obvious that I have answered you in a way that you were not expecting, which shows how stupid you are, and you did not—

Catty-Corner: My point is that if the job of a police officer becomes to risk that which he himself regards as the *most* important then the position will soon be either wanting or warped into nonrecognition. The truth is that the nearer is placed importance then the further will we continue to drift from one another, and if, for example, that intruder who broke into your home were to—

Me: I know that you are trying to scare me, but you can stop because it will not work. I already told you that it is the job of police officers to do the things that you are talking about, and you are sometimes so—

Catty-Corner: Well, if that police officer's *most* important might be threatened then why would he not quit his job? Should his *most* important not be his *most* important? In fact, why would *anyone* ever again answer a call for help? Why should others remain stupid sacrificials for your selfish self? There is, after all, not a better—

Me: I already told you that I will not let you scare me, so it is obvious that you have not been listening to me at all. You are the opposite of what I need to feel better, and I knew that I should not have—

Catty-Corner: The reason why the world feels as if it is becoming scarier every day is because it is, in fact, doing that very thing, and the descent is caused by the fact that our expectations demand for it to be so.

Me: Well, you cannot say that I did not hear you out, which I know that you will still do, but I am not going to listen to anything else.

ON RIGHTEOUSNESS

Me: Morning, neighbor.

My Catty-Corner Neighbor: Good morning.

Me: This briskness in the air sure feels nice. It feels like the world itself is insisting on movement.

Catty-Corner: I am content just as long as it does not rain.

Me: That is not exactly the highest of bars.

Catty-Corner: Well, that is why it refers to contentment. Being content means being less than happy, after all.

Me: I am not so sure that that is right. In fact, I cannot think of anyone who would be content with less than happiness.

Catty-Corner: Well, as true as that may be then it still cannot bully truth. Enough people being wrong never changes the nature of right, and if everyone is wrong then that is just the way that it is. No strength of wrongness ever achieves righteousness.

Me: […]

Catty-Corner: [...]

Me: That was a funny word to hear you use.

Catty-Corner: Which?

Me: *Righteousness*. It was odd to even watch it come out of your mouth.

Catty-Corner: Well, I suppose that it is a somewhat funny word for anyone to ever use.

Me: I meant specifically for you.

Catty-Corner: What do you mean?

Me: Well, it is like hearing a sinner preach, I suppose. It feels out of place, in other words, in a sacrilegious way, and I would, in fact, say that the only thing that you are ever righter than is the government.

Catty-Corner: Well, I would hope so.

Me: I am sure that you do. You would be selfish like that, and it also does not surprise me at all to find out that you are at such an extreme of selfishness that you have no problem admitting it. You even prefer it when the government is in the wrong, I bet, since it gives you something to complain about, and you are probably one of those who tries to exploit it, too.

Catty-Corner: Of course not. A wrong government is even more dangerous than a wronged one, though it is a narrow margin as well as rather fluid.

Me: Then what is it that you want? Do you want the government to be in the right?

Catty-Corner: Of course not.

Me: Then that means that you must want it to be in the wrong.

Catty-Corner: Of course not.

Me: That does not make any sense at all. You are just hiding behind this—

Catty-Corner: Are right and wrong the only things that a government can be? What about a government that did not concern itself with *either* of them?

Me: What do you mean?

Catty-Corner: Well, I would say that I want my government to be concerned with *legal* and *illegal*, not right and wrong. If you want to talk about righteousness then go to a chapel, not the Capitol. It is important to remember that just because we all have stopped attending church does not mean that the state must erect a steeple. Righteousness has no place in government, and any government that concerns itself with it becomes, by rule, tyrannical. Demanding the government to do what is right is thus the same as demanding it to do what is wrong, and if there ever was a better—

Me: It is good to know that you have no moral compass. You are lucky that you are saying this to me rather than anyone else because most people would not let—

Catty-Corner: I have a moral compass, but the difference between us is that I regard mine as a personal responsibility, and you believe yours to be a political apportionment. The difference lies in whether you believe that you should affect the state or the state should infect you.

Me: I cannot believe that you are actually trying to argue that government should be immoral and that you are willing—

Catty-Corner: I want government to *amoral*, and it is, in fact, the only legitimate way for a government to be.

Me: Does that mean that you would say that a government that only ever did what was right was illegitimate?

Catty-Corner: Of course.

Me: That is backwards.

Catty-Corner: What do you mean?

Me: Well, it is obvious. Anyone would tell you that a government should always do what is right because there is not anyone who is stupid enough to—

Catty-Corner: Are you referring to *representative* government? I have assumed as much so far, but I just want to make sure.

Me: Of course. We are talking about good government, after all.

Catty-Corner: I see. Does that mean that you are saying that a representative government should at the same time be a good government?

Me: Of course. It is not just me saying this, either. If you ask anyone then they will tell you the same thing. You have not said anything that even sounds like it is trying to be convincing, anyway.

Catty-Corner: Well, it is not about how we want things to be but rather how they are. It is possible, after all, for an individual to accept and even advance ideas that are not in his immediate interest.

Me: I am going to leave if you are not going to actually listen to me. You just want to insult me, and you do not care about what I have to say, which should not surprise me, I suppose, but it still makes me feel—

Catty-Corner: Do there exist wrong individuals in the world?

Me: What do you mean?

Catty-Corner: Well, are there those who you would say are wrong? This wrongness can be about anything, and it could be factual, or it could be moral, or—

Me: Of course. I have never said that there are not wrong people, so do not try to put those words in my mouth. No one would ever try to make that argument. Those who are right usually have the experience of some resistance, after all. We are talking about what government should do, though, so I do not see why it matters.

Catty-Corner: Well, how would these *wrong* people be given representation in your *righteous* government?

Me: Like anyone else, of course.

Catty-Corner: Even though they are wrong?

Me: What do you mean?

Catty-Corner: Well, is it not obvious? The truth is that a righteous government can never be representative because it will never have a fully righteous citizenry to represent. If you are right and I am wrong then the righteous government *must* take your side just as the representative government *must not* take either of our sides. The righteous government counts claims while the representative government counts votes, and each has in its very nature a blind spot for the other. If two

142

lose to a righteous one then the thing is not representative, and if two beat a righteous one then the thing is not righteous. You can have your government be either representative or righteous, but an expectation of both is an inevitable slide into neither.

Me: You are twisting words.

Catty-Corner: Are you sure? I think rather that you have twisted them yourself for so long that you no longer even see them as bent. If a righteous government cannot be wrong then it cannot be representative, and if a representative government is ever wrong then it cannot be righteous. It is important to remember that the presence of wrong people is what necessitates the existence of wrong government, and if we look at it from the other way then it becomes—

Me: These are things that I should not have to help you with. Everyone knows them, and they are even easy to figure out on one's own, too. All I can say is that I am glad that I now know how you feel about government.

Catty-Corner: My point is that a *righteous* expectation of *representative* government is a wrong one by way of impossibility. It is, in other words, the crossroads of two opposing ideals, and its X marks a spot that can never be reached. The truth is that any righteous government that cloaks itself in the representative is *always* doing so as a cover, and any representative government that cloaks itself in the righteous is *always* doing so as a filler. After all, there is not—

Me: I have to go. I think that we are done talking, anyway.

Catty-Corner: Are you headed somewhere?

Me: I just want to get an early start on my day.

Catty-Corner: I see. Well, I await your counterargument. Are you available this evening?

Me: I do not think so. I might be free sometime tomorrow, but I will likely be busy.

ON AMENDMENTS

Me: Morning, neighbor.

My Catty-Corner Neighbor: Good morning.

Me: Are you headed out for a run?

Catty-Corner: I am. I find that it has almost become necessary.

Me: I would agree with that. No one could doubt that our season's latest trend is fitness, and the unfit are finally those who are so.

Catty-Corner: That may be true. It is not why I am running, though. Instead, I find it to be the best way to force the anger out of me as early in the morning as possible.

Me: What do you mean?

Catty-Corner: Well, are you not paying attention?

Me: I pay attention to things far more than you do. In fact, I am usually the one who has to inform you of anything that happens in the world. I am not sure what it is that you are angry about, anyway.

Catty-Corner: Did you see that there was another mass shooting?

Me: I did see that. I am, however, surprised to hear that you care.

Catty-Corner: I care in a way other than exploitation.

Me: Do not start getting like that. I am sure that I want to get rid of guns just as much as you do.

Catty-Corner: Well, that is good. I was worried that I was going to have to defend the Bills of Rights in an argument with an American. It really is alarming when the greatest of shields must itself be shielded from those behind it.

Me: What do you mean?

Catty-Corner: I mean that I am glad to hear that you are as much of a supporter of the Second Amendment as I am.

Me: […]

Catty-Corner: […]

Me: What I am a supporter of is sense.

Catty-Corner: That is what I said.

Me: […]

Catty-Corner: [...]

Me: Lives are not sense to you. That is good to know.

Catty-Corner: Well, I would say that it is good to know the extent of your thought. Are you able to identify for me an argument against the Second Amendment other than safety concerns?

Me: The fact that you would need any more reasons shows just how bad you are. Do you really have no empathy at all?

Catty-Corner: I often worry that I have too much.

Me: I bet that you really do. You probably find some way to actually do so. That sounds *exactly* like the type of person that you are, and I bet—

Catty-Corner: It is important to remember that disliking me is not itself a counterargument.

Me: Well, what even is your argument? I bet that you do not have an actual one.

Catty-Corner: My only argument is that if you want to get rid of one Amendment in light of safety concerns then maybe there is another Amendment or two that *I* want to get rid of for the same reasons.

Me: What do you mean?

Catty-Corner: Well, are you aware of the Fourth Amendment?

Me: Is that the one about searches?

Catty-Corner: That is correct.

Me: You want to get rid of it?

Catty-Corner: [...]

Me: Well, do you?

Catty-Corner: I would not act first, but I would be willing to follow an example down that path.

Me: What do you mean?

Catty-Corner: Well, if the Second Amendment must fall to safety concerns then it is clear that the Fourth must fall along with it. After all, think of all the harm that that Amendment does.

Me: That Amendment does not do harm. In fact, it keeps people from being harmed.

Catty-Corner: What about the bad eggs? Would you not, after all, admit that there are those who do not use the Amendment for its intended purposes?

Me: That is just the way that things work, though. You cannot decide to scrap something good just because some people use it for bad.

Catty-Corner: What about in the face of safety?

Me: What do you mean?

Catty-Corner: Well, consider, for example, drugs. It certainly is not any secret that illegal drugs are prevalent in the country, and such a statement is so obvious that it does not require any argument. I would, in fact, doubt that you would be able to find a single street in any neighborhood that you would be able to drive down while confident that you were not cutting through a sea of contraband. The prevalence of illegal drugs is thus unquestionable, and we can easily address their harm, which is equally unquestionable. After all, which kills a greater number between guns and drugs? Drugs do, of course. Which harms a greater number? Drugs do, of course. Which—

Me: Do you really think that it is that simple?

Catty-Corner: Is it not? If one thing must be rolled back for safety then must not other, similar things be similarly rolled back, particularly when greater violators? Drugs unquestionably both harm more and kill more than guns. This does not even count the number of lives derailed by drugs, or how about the literally incalculable number of our nation's children who have their formative years warped by drugs, either from pressured usage or an addled parent? Does the harm done to them matter less simply because it is reported less? Is the vehemence of a news story the greatest determinant in how it is read? Are you able to state any reason for why their harm matters less other than the fact that you have obviously decided to care about it less? You happen to have an affinity for the thing that hurts them, so that makes it more acceptable than the thing that you worry could hurt you? The truth is that you do not want—

Me: Why do you even want guns? Make that point.

Catty-Corner: Well, I would say that the reasons in the Amendment itself are a good place to start. *A well-regulated militia being*—

Me: That is what I thought. Your argument is so antiquated that it has its own powdered wig. What you are talking about may have been true back in the past when the world was different, but it is just an excuse now. Militia is not even a word with meaning anymore.

Catty-Corner: What do you mean?

Me: Well, it is just the way that things are. Are you aware that guns have advanced in the last two hundred years? The idea of some militia holding off *any* modern army is ridiculous, and everyone knows that, so it is not a valid point.

Catty-Corner: Does that apply to Vietnam and the Middle East, too? It is important to remember that the arguments made today must make sense with the ones made yesterday, and if you argue that an army's invasion is doomed because it will be impossible for them to police the invaded area then you must admit that that army's own land will have the same issue in the event that they decide to turn, march, and make occupation.

Me: It is not important, anyway. The point is that people just use the ideals of being for guns as an excuse for trying to make sure that they can have what they want. They are exploiting the fear of something for their own benefit.

Catty-Corner: I see.

Me: Do you?

Catty-Corner: Your view? Not at all.

Me: Of course not. I knew that you would not, and I still wasted my time, which is my fault, I suppose, since I knew that it would happen, but—

Catty-Corner: Do you see *my* view?

Me: Of course not. Why would you even ask me that?

Catty-Corner: Well, if you do not see mine then why does the fact of my not seeing yours seem to be considered by you to be an argument against me on its own?

Me: One of our views cheers people dying, and the other is mine. That is the difference. Bad ideas are obviously different from good ones, and I do not understand how you can be having so much trouble with this. Anyone else would know what I was talking about.

Catty-Corner: I see.

Me: I am *sure* that you do.

Catty-Corner: Are you, at the very least, willing to admit that the Fourth Amendment *must* be tossed out along with the Second? In fact, a further point in favor of why the Fourth is even more deserving of removal is the simple fact that it is merely the fourth in line rather than the second. Then there is, of course, the fact of the arguments against the Fourth being more statistically valid.

Me: Do you honestly want the police to be able to come into your home whenever they want and for whatever reason?

Catty-Corner: Can you honestly tell me that we would not be a safer country if they were to do so? If the police were, for example, to toss every home like a cell every few months then would that not be a sound steppingstone toward safety's guiding light? How about

152

if it was every month, or once a week, or randomly? Each of these could, after all, be claimed to be further advancements toward that bespeckled beacon that you have so fixed in the sky. If you want then they could be on the lookout for guns, too.

Me: Are you saying that you just automatically want whatever seems safer on the surface?

Catty-Corner: I think that I meant to ask you that same question earlier.

Me: What if the police decide to arrest more than just the guilty during their tossing of homes? Or what if they decide to look for other things than just what we want them to? What if I need to stand up for myself, but I cannot because there is a new expectation of being at all times subject—

Catty-Corner: Now that I think about it, there is a line in the First Amendment that I want scratched, too. Mass attacks, after all, only *most* of the time involve guns, but they every time involve masses. If people did not assemble then they could not be attacked in mass, so those few words are an easy removal. I know that this one is part of a higher Amendment, but it has this and several other points in its favor as far as its removal's closer relations with safety. The Second Amendment better get in line because safety is going to have to work through a lot just to get to it.

Me: Well, I can see that you are not being serious, and you were probably not being serious the whole time, which means that you were just trying to waste my time, so congratulations to you for being successful in that, I suppose, but I will not let—

Catty-Corner: My arguments have been the same as yours, though there have been, of course, those places where they have been more valid.

Me: I am sure that you actually think that.

Catty-Corner: Could you share your counterargument with me for how you know otherwise?

Me: I am not going to waste any more of my time talking to you today.

Catty-Corner: Well, I await your counterargument.

Me: You would probably just decide to misunderstand it.

ON ANECDOTES

Me: Morning, neighbor.

My Catty-Corner Neighbor: Good morning. It is good to see you. I hope that you are enjoying that coffee of yours.

Me: I am. It is just what I needed to get going this morning. How are you enjoying that slice of yours? I know that it is just what you needed.

Catty-Corner: What do you mean?

Me: I mean your *slice*.

Catty-Corner: […]

Me: Your slice of humble pie.

Catty-Corner: What do you mean?

Me: Well, it should be obvious to even you, I think. We were arguing yesterday, and I proved you wrong, and then on the news last night was even further proof. The very thing that we were talking about happened again, so you must now admit that I was right. How many more times does it have to happen before you admit that I have irrefutable proof?

Catty-Corner: I told you yesterday that your argument is only an anecdotal one, so your announcement today of further anecdotes means nothing. There is, after all, not a—

Me: Just because something may be part of an anecdote does not mean that it is anecdotal.

Catty-Corner: Well, just because something occurs to you does not mean that it is *not* anecdotal.

Me: That does not make any sense at all. In fact, I bet that you are probably even agreeing with me without realizing it, which sometimes happens whenever you try to be smarter than you actually are.

Catty-Corner: My point is that what you are paying attention to is *never* also that which is going on. It is important to remember that you could, for example, assemble one million of your neighbors, and even this group that is too large to be able to know in a lifetime will only constitute less than one percent of the country. They could even all bring a friend, and you would still be well short of any amount that would statistically matter. There exists, therefore, complexity beyond measure, and this is the reason why there is no such thing as an actually indicative instance. It is, in other words, an issue of going one step beyond that of the personal-Jesus to that of the Jesus-as-self, which will—

Me: You are *still* not making any sense, and if you are just trying to avoid admitting that I was right all along then you do not, I suppose, have to because I already know it. I do not need anyone to tell me what I already know, after all.

Catty-Corner: I see.

Me: You are making me not want to tell the story that I came out to tell you. You are like this every day, and I wonder how many more things you would know about if you did not make yourself so distasteful.

Catty-Corner: What is the story?

Me: Well, it is more just something interesting that I heard and wanted to share with you. It is a good conversation piece, so I have been bringing it up a lot.

Catty-Corner: [...]

Me: I am not sure who the first person who said it was, but all you have to do is realize that there are two possibilities that can exist as far as universal existence. The first is that we are entirely alone in the universe, and the second is that aliens exist, and to find out either of them would be terrifying.

Catty-Corner: [...]

Me: Are you still trying to comprehend it? It took even me a while to wrap my head around it the first time that

I heard it, so I would not be surprised if it took you twice as long, but you are, I bet, just trying to come up with some unimportant way that it is wrong rather than actually listening to—

Catty-Corner: Well, I would say that I find it to be more *worrisome* than *wrong*. After all, its rightness only depends on the hollowness of its speaker while it is corrosive in its very expression. It is an either-or situation that shows that its questioner does not grasp the overall situation, and it is a marvel that we have made ourselves so lonely that we actually wonder whether we are alone. The truth is that one's nearest neighbors constitute complexities beyond even the biggest of space's explosions, and one wonders just how deep of a shut-in you must be to deny to them the very things that you look for in both yourself and the stars. It is important to remember both that none of us is alone and that none of us ever was. To wonder at what may be out there is, therefore, akin to—

Me: I am going back inside. The only thing that I wanted to do was to share something interesting with you, and you have tried to—

Catty-Corner: Well, all I wanted to do was share something interesting *about* you, and you will always try to—

Me: That does not make any sense at all, but it does not matter, anyway. I was right about what we were arguing about, so that is what is important. If you are not going to admit it then I am not going to listen to anything else.

Catty-Corner: […]

Me: I knew that you would not be willing to do it.

ON ARTISTRY

Me: Evening, neighbor.

My Catty-Corner Neighbor: Good evening.

Me: How was your trip back to your old campus? I have not seen you, so I remembered that it was today. You must have been welcomed back, I bet. Were you treated like a former conqueror?

Catty-Corner: Well, I was actually less noticeable than the conquered during those undergraduate years of mine.

Me: That cannot be true. I am sure that you would make yourself heard, even if numbered among those who are not supposed to be. If told to listen then you talk, and if told to talk then you talk about things that no one would ever want to hear. You would never, I think, let anyone tell you otherwise, no matter the age or time.

Catty-Corner: [...]

Me: Was your trip back actually that bad?

Catty-Corner: Not at all. It was nice to see things that I had not for so long, and I had the chance to see those whom I did not think that I would ever see again. There was, I suppose, one part of my visit back that was not perfect, however.

Me: What do you mean?

Catty-Corner: There was a large installation in the middle of campus that confused me, and I could not figure out what it meant. I stared at it for almost an hour, and I walked around to all its sides, but I could not find a view of its meaning. It was a large mass of broken ski poles that were glued together up into the sky, but they did not appear to take the shape of anything. I looked at how the poles were glued, too, but they did not seem to have a uniformity or any skillful skirting of it. I do not like to feel stupid, so I kept—

Me: Well, if you do not like to feel stupid then you should not so often court stupidity. Anyone would be able to tell that you were looking at an art installation. I do not even have to see it to know, and you should actually—

Catty-Corner: How do you know whether it was art?

Me: Because it is obvious. Art installations are put up on campuses all the time, which is something that everyone knows.

Catty-Corner: Well, how do you know whether it was art?

Me: What do you mean?

Catty-Corner: I mean that you do not know what it was supposed to be, so how do you know what it is? In fact, I was there and still—

Me: Why does it have to be something to be art? Not everything has to have a meaning, which includes art, which is something that everyone knows. Art, after all, happens all the time, and you can see it everywhere. Every single time that a person expresses himself then art gets made, and I should not have to be—

Catty-Corner: Self-expression is not art, and that is why they are different words. One can, after all, express oneself without creating art in the same way that one can create art that has an expression beyond oneself. It is also important to remember that art must have *some* criteria for its definition since we already have a word for everything, which is, after all, *everything*.

Me: You are not making any sense at all, which is what you are trying to do, I bet. I know that all you want to do is to make it seem like art can only be the things that you approve of, which is always the reason whenever someone attacks art. Everyone knows that art can be anything and that it happens every day, and everyone also knows—

Catty-Corner: The truth is that if no wrong is involved then no art can be. Take, for example, the *art* installation that I saw on campus since if it was, instead, a monument of self-expression then—

Me: I am not going to listen to any more of this. It is obvious that you are wrong, and this is not what I need to be hearing, anyway. I will, I think, see—

Catty-Corner: The last thing that I want to say is that nothing ventured means that nothing can be attained, and art, in fact, far more often features the expression of *others* than it does oneself. To shape to nothing is to sink below evaluation, and if you cannot see how a thing escaped error then you should not see it as a question of quality. After all, if a thing could not have been bad then how can you ever know whether it is good? If it was not possible to do wrong then why should anyone be impressed by the done right? The potential for incorrectness is a prerequisite for—

Me: I want you to know that I have not been listening to any of what you are saying.

ON DEGREES

Me: Morning, neighbor.

My Catty-Corner Neighbor: Good morning.

Me: Why do look like you are not celebrating? Have you not heard the news?

Catty-Corner: What do you mean?

Me: Student loan debt is going to be cancelled. They announced it this morning. Did you really not hear about it? The government is finally doing what we all always wanted it to do.

Catty-Corner: When is it going to happen?

Me: Well, we have to wait for them to announce that part of it. They said that it is definitely going to happen, though. I saw it said as a promise by multiple—

Catty-Corner: Do you have a lot of student loans?

Me: I used to, but most of mine have already been paid off. It would have been better for me to have made better use of that money, of course, since there were a lot of things that I would have been able to buy with those dollars that went to loan payments, but I can still take advantage of some of the relief. I am not, after all, one of those who thinks that others should have to suffer just because I was able to pull myself out of suffering, so I am not against it.

Catty-Corner: Does that mean that you will allow your student loans to be repudiated?

Me: Of course. Everyone will, so it would be stupid not to. I know that—

Catty-Corner: Does that mean that you will be repudiating your degree or, at the very least, a calculated portion of it?

Me: What do you mean?

Catty-Corner: Well, if they will be returning your money then will you be returning what that money bought?

Me: Of course not. If I did not have my degree then I would lose my job.

Catty-Corner: I see.

Me: Well, it is obvious that you are looking at it wrong, which is what you always decide to do. This is not about us having something taken away, but, instead, it is about them returning what they stole.

Catty-Corner: It was, however, stolen with consent and to mutual benefit, though, which means that we have—

Me: The only *benefit* was to them, and everyone knows that. They make billions of dollars off us, and all we get is wasted years of our lives. I could have been out making money during the four years that I was in college, after all.

Catty-Corner: If that is true then why are you not willing to give up your degree? Why should you enjoy the association without meeting the obligation?

Me: Did you not listen to what I just said? If I did not have my degree then I would get fired. It was one of the requirements in the job listing, after all, so they probably would not have even brought me in for an interview without it.

Catty-Corner: Does that mean that a college degree is valuable?

Me: Of course. A degree is obviously valuable, and there is no one who would say otherwise. That is why it is so wrong for them to charge so much for it.

Catty-Corner: I see.

Me: I know that you do not. You are going to try to make it seem like I am against education, but what I am actually against is people having to pay so much for it.

It is wrong for them to have something that we need and to make money off—

Catty-Corner: Is a degree something that is necessary for life?

Me: It is in the modern world. If you want to live anything that is close to a good—

Catty-Corner: Does that mean that those without degrees are dead?

Me: What do you mean?

Catty-Corner: Well, if a degree is necessary for life then do those who fall short of it fall into oblivion? Is expulsion, in other words, akin to execution? Is there—

Me: Of course not. No one should ever feel as if there is only one correct path to life, and I know—

Catty-Corner: Does that mean that a degree is *helpful* to life rather than necessary for it?

Me: Well, that may be true, but it does not change—

Catty-Corner: Does that mean that degrees are things that we *want*? You said earlier that they are things that we *need*. There is a difference between the two, and it is a very—

Me: There is not a difference between the two at all. It is only a slight difference of words, and you are trying to turn it into something else. When something is wanted bad enough then it becomes necessary, which means that it is a need. This is something that everyone knows, and no one else would need to hear me explain the whole thing.

Catty-Corner: I see.

Me: Well, what I see is that I have let you waste enough of my time this morning. Everyone else will be happy to hear happy news, I bet, and I will not have—

Catty-Corner: It is important to remember that *helpful* and *needed* are words as far apart as *right* and *privilege*. After all, that which is valuable is that which, by rule, none has a right to, and the placement of emphasis is—

Me: If you had valued your own degree a little more then maybe we would not have to have this argument. You were probably—

Catty-Corner: Well, you may have to prove to me that I ever actually saw value. The truth is that education's spreading and simultaneous stunting have resulted in the world being covered by a thin paste, and the reason why we have become so alienated from our own heads is because we have been given framed rectangles of paper telling us to be so. It has become so bad in some places that—

Me: I have spent enough time trying to get you to celebrate, I think. Today is supposed to be a good day, after all, and you—

Catty-Corner: Will you tell me your counterargument before you go? It would, after all, be helpful for me to know the way in which an unpaid degree is not a purloined one since—

Me: I have already spent too much of my morning doing that very thing. If you are too stupid to see how a free degree will affect you then maybe it is not for you.

Catty-Corner: I see. Well, I await your counterargument.

Me: You can go and get it from anyone, and you will not need to get a loan for it, either.

ON SCHOOLING

Me: Morning, neighbor.

My Catty-Corner Neighbor: Good morning. It is good to see you. Did you have a—

Me: We are not going to talk about whatever you want today. I have a question that you will be forced to squirm under because it is the perfect trap, and I have already decided that you are going to have to answer it.

Catty-Corner: [...]

Me: Are you not going to try to avoid it? I promise that I will not let you escape once I ask it.

Catty-Corner: [...]

Me: Well, it is obvious that you do not even have the—

Catty-Corner: Ask your question. I am ready for it.

Me: I want to know what you think should be taught to our nation's children. Should, for example, the country teach kids that the Civil War was a righteous fight against original sin, or should they be told that things have never actually—

Catty-Corner: Are there only two options to the question?

Me: What do you mean?

Catty-Corner: Well, is it acceptable to answer that the country should make *no* decision on what should be thought of it? No matter what one thinks, after all, it is better to have thought, and it is important to remember that no opinion of the Civil War can ever be worse than *any* forced opinion of it. One wonders at what point government will cease being a revenge-tipped club that either side clambers over—

Me: I knew that I should not have asked you a question that related to history. Your only interest in things is to try to twist them into your own points, and you are, I bet, even one of those who follow the *Great Man* theory of history.

Catty-Corner: Of course. There is, in fact, not another theory that is—

Me: I knew it. You are the—

Catty-Corner: Any indictment against the *Great Man* theory is as connotational as it is superficial. Its objectors, after all, concern themselves solely with its name, and their issue ranges merely from the word *great* to the word *man*. If, for example, the theory was, instead, called the *Individual Actor* theory then it would not have any of its current trouble. In fact, with the way that we now worship the stars of screen then it would, I bet, be considered taboo to even question the differently-named theory, and those who did so would likely find themselves blackballed. The catchiness of a thing's name has become the greatest indicator of its success, so it should not be surprising that—

Me: If you actually knew anything about history then you would not even think these things. Everyone knows that the bad histories were those of the past, not the present. Historians, after all, now actually take the time to write people's histories that are—

Catty-Corner: Is it not odd that those *people's* histories are those most filled with quotes? There are obviously *certain* individuals who those authors regard as worthy of—

Me: That is not important at all. We are talking about your stupid idea that history is made by *great men*, which is so obviously—

Catty-Corner: History is made by *great men* by way of the word *great* meaning *impactful on history* and by way of the word *men* meaning *member of mankind*. It is, therefore, a rather wide definition, and that is why—

Me: It is obviously wrong, though, and everyone knows that individual people do not affect—

Catty-Corner: The truth is that history may be guided by masses and millennia, but it is determined by individuals and instance, and it is a thing that stretches back from us as a lengthy series of individuals correcting the world. After all, to cite, for example, a particular famine as the cause of a particular revolt requires the explanation of why *all* famines did not lead to similar revolts, and to interpret history through the actions of masses is to—

Me: This is not—

Catty-Corner: The truth is that every hungry stomach grumbles differently, and to equate them all is a disservice akin to ignoring each one. Is not every *mass*, after all, made up of *individuals*, and is not every *individual*, after all, merely made up of—

Me: None of this is what I wanted to talk about.

ON SPEEDING

Me: Evening, neighbor.

My Catty-Corner Neighbor: Good evening. You are home early.

Me: Well, that is true, I suppose. I should have been back even earlier, though.

Catty-Corner: Was there traffic today?

Me: There is traffic every day. I usually get in the far-left lane, however, so I tend to avoid the worst of it.

Catty-Corner: What made today different?

Me: There was a car in the far-left lane that should not have been there.

Catty-Corner: What do you mean?

Me: It was going too slow. It was going *far* too slow, in fact.

Catty-Corner: How fast was it going?

Me: It was hardly going the speed limit.

Catty-Corner: I see.

Me: I happened to get behind the car, and then I could not get around it. I followed behind as close as I could to its bumper, of course, so that the driver would know that I was annoyed, but it never moved over into the slower lanes. I was stuck behind it for several miles, and there was a whole line of other cars behind me, too, so it was not just me who was stuck going only a little over sixty miles per hour. I sometimes have trouble remembering that there are actually people who are so self-centered and oblivious to others, but then I have an interaction with someone like that, and it brings every—

Catty-Corner: What is the speed limit there?

Me: It is sixty miles per hour all along that part of the freeway. Did you really not know that, or is this—

Catty-Corner: Does that mean that the car in front of you was, at the very least, traveling at the speed limit?

Me: Of course. I just told you that that was the whole problem.

Catty-Corner: Does that mean that you wanted to go faster than the speed limit?

Me: Of course. I was not the only one, too, so if you are going to try to make me feel bad about it then you will not be able to. This is, after all, the far-left lane that we are talking about.

Catty-Corner: What do you mean?

Me: Everyone knows what I mean. It is obvious that you are just playing stupid since you do not actually have anything to say, and it is also obvious that your hope is that I get annoyed enough to be distracted into allowing you to escape unargued. Everyone knows that slower cars are supposed to move out of the way of faster ones. It is, in fact, the whole point of the far-left lane.

Catty-Corner: Does the far-left lane have a different speed limit?

Me: Of course not. That would not make any sense at all since it is still the same road.

Catty-Corner: Does that mean that you were attempting to break the law today, and this other car was in your way? If that is true then such defenders of order are, I think, usually hailed as heroes, and they are, at the very least, called *vigilantes* since they take upon themselves that which should—

Me: We are talking about speeding, not law breaking. Everyone knows that there is a difference between the two, and you are the only person who would ever try to make someone feel bad about something that everyone does. I only speed when I am in a hurry, anyway, so I am not like those people who speed everywhere they go.

Catty-Corner: I see.

Me: You do not get to decide when others are in a hurry.

Catty-Corner: Well, you should not get to decide others' exposure to that hurry.

Me: What do you mean?

Catty-Corner: Well, if it is wrong for the slow driver to take your time into his hands then would it not also be wrong for the fast driver to do the same with your life? In fact, would it not be *more* wrong? It is, after all, the slow drivers who waste minutes, but it is the fast drivers who waste lives.

Me: You are looking at it wrong, and I am not sure why you are having so much trouble with this. Speeding is different from breaking the law, which is what—

Catty-Corner: The truth is that one's driving is the best window into his civic soul. Speed limits are, after all, a citizen's most frequent as well as most typical of brushes with the law since we interact with them every day as well as every second that we are behind the wheel, and it is also important to remember that a speed limit is that which every driver is aware of as well as that which every driver is empowered over. A speed limit is, therefore, a common, unceremonious interaction with government wherein the citizen is fully versed in the law as well as fully in control over his actions, and it is for these reasons that a speed limit is the most accurate of indicators into the—

Me: I know that you have probably forgotten, but I was home early, so every second that I waste here with you lessens that earliness. If you want to ramble then you can stay out here by yourself, and I will let—

Catty-Corner: My point is that speed limits tell a lot about us, and the fact that we have forced a country-wide expectation of going five miles per hour over them tells even more. The truth is that we all say that we want some form of *law and order*, but any look into our behavior proves that we display an utter unwillingness to order ourselves beneath the law. *Law and order*, therefore, is not what we want. Instead, we want things ordered to our liking and laws without the audacity to intrude.

Me: I do not think that I heard the end of that last sentence, but it does not matter since I will not hear any more. I am sure that it did not make any sense, anyway, since that is where you always take—

Catty-Corner: My point is that there is not—

Me: I just said that I will hear no more.

ON GAMBLING

Me: Evening, neighbor.

My Catty-Corner Neighbor: Good evening.

Me: I can promise that you are the only one who thinks so.

Catty-Corner: That cannot be true. It must be the nicest night that we have had so far this year, and I have, in fact, seen quite a few families out walking together in the sunset.

Me: Well, the only reason that they are outside is because they are too angry to stay inside, I bet. Everyone lost money today.

Catty-Corner: What do you mean?

Me: The stock market took another dip.

Catty-Corner: […]

Me: It is all part of this big dive that has been happening lately.

Catty-Corner: Is that a bad thing?

Me: How can you even say that? I know that you are not being serious, but it is still not something that you should say. You should not even think it.

Catty-Corner: Gambled gambles being gambled away do not seem that shocking to me.

Me: We are talking about the stock market, not gambling.

Catty-Corner: I see.

Me: The stock market is not some seedy, barren backroom, which is the caricature that you seem to have of it, and I would be willing to bet that the only reason is because someone told you that it is that way. You were told that it is bad, so you believe that it is bad, and that is as far as you will go. The truth is that the stock market is a place of business.

Catty-Corner: Well, a casino is a place of business, too.

Me: That is not the same at all. A casino is a whole system designed to steal money from people and then feed it to those who have no interest in actually working for it. Casinos are designed to *take* money while the stock market is designed to *make* money. That is the difference, and I was actually able to say it in a simple and easy to understand way, which is something that you are never able to do with any of the points that you try to make.

Catty-Corner: Is it possible for wealth to be gained other than by its loss elsewhere?

Me: That may be the stupidest thing that you have ever said, and it shows that you do not know the first thing about money. Even a child knows that it is not a zero-sum game.

Catty-Corner: Well, children are often those most targeted by advertising.

Me: What do you mean?

Catty-Corner: My point is that the making of money may not be a zero-sum game, but *wealth* certainly is. The very existence of the haves is defined by the have-nots, after all, and the more that the have-nots have then the more must the haves raise the definition of naught. A millionaire among millionaires is not wealthy just as a billionaire among billionaires is not. Instead, it is the billionaire among millionaires who is wealthy, and it is the millionaire among billionaires who is poor. Wealth is not a counted but rather a comparative thing. If I, for example, were to—

Me: I do not need to hear any example from you. I already know that whatever you say is going to be wrong because everyone knows of the zero-sum fallacy. It is obvious, and you will not find a single person who does not know about it. It is, in fact, so obvious that you should not even have to think about it.

You should have listened more back when you were in school so that you would not have to spend your adult life wasting the time of others like—

Catty-Corner: The zero-sum fallacy is itself a fallacy in the most sinister sense of the word. It is a lie told because the tellers do not like the very appearance of the truth. Take, for example, the absurd notion that wealth is created. This premise can only be accepted if you are willing to take a perverted view of wealth that has been stretched on the rack of self-interest. The truth is that it is *things* that are created, never wealth. Every new product brought to market is not in itself new wealth being dumped into the world. Instead, a change in wealth is caused by a new product that your neighbor gets and that you envy. Wealth is an interpersonal thing, and it is the word *rich* that refers to the intrapersonal side of the matter. These two words are often used interchangeably, but they are very different, and it is a very important distinction. Rich is what one can be in a vacuum while one can never have wealth in the same situation. It is money in great amounts that qualifies one as rich, but it is money in *greater* amounts that qualifies him as wealthy. Riches are defined by more while wealth is defined by more *than*. One can be rich with money, but he can only have wealth with purchasing power. The one-dollar man who acquires a second dollar has become richer, but there is much more about his situation that we will have to know before declaring that he was become any wealthier. The two-dollar man who loses one of them has become less rich, but there is much more about his situation that we will have to know before declaring that he has become any less wealthy.

Me: You keep repeating yourself, but you cannot make any sense even while doing so. You can say stupid things and try to make them seem smart all you want, but if the substance is not there then people will never care. The whole thing is called the zero-sum *fallacy*, after all, which means that it is pointing out an error in thinking. All you have to do is read the name to know that, but you always think of yourself as being so much smarter than everyone else, so you do not even take the time to think of all the little things along the way to whatever stupid point you are trying to make. Wealth is created every single—

Catty-Corner: How can wealth *ever* be created when it is contextual? Riches are the amounts, and wealth is the interplay of those amounts. There is the same amount of wealth in the world today as there was yesterday and the day before. Wealth gained here is, by rule, wealth lost there, and the reason why you are told otherwise is because those who do so want you to be satisfied with increasing riches while they satisfy themselves with increasing wealth. You are told that wealth can be created because it is something that they do not want you to pursue, and they want you to think that it will naturally come to you in your turn so that you will patiently await that turn. The truth is that the longer the expectation remains one of ever-increasing wealth then the ever-wider will be the realization of the bitterness gulf between those—

Me: None of this is important, anyway. We were talking about the stock market, so I am not sure how you got so off topic. The stock market is not about winners and losers, and everyone knows that. It is a place for people to invest their—

Catty-Corner: It is a place for some to *invest* and others to *divest*. It has always been that way, and it will always be that way. Losers exist even if you do not like the appellation, after all, and ignoring them because you do not want to see them means that you yourself are one of those who holds them down. The idea of everyone at once being able to win the country-wide carny game is so absurd that it is surprising that its contrivers ever dared even—

Me: It is you who is the absurd one. You probably like the idea of people having money stolen from them, so that is why you are arguing for it. It is so—

Catty-Corner: If the stock market produces nothing but winners then where are they? Does it not, after all, often occur that a *winner* of the stock market is joined by so many other *winners* and thus finds out that his *winnings* were only enough to break even, and is gaining nothing while having put something in not the very definition of a *loser*? What about the lost time, too? Taking time to get nowhere is a double loss, after all. The truth is that if you believe that everyone can at once win then you yourself are likely the euphemized loser. To put money into the stock market is not in any way a sure thing, but it has been advertised as such for long enough that it has become the expectation, which itself has grown into causing the putting of money into the stock market to become a practical necessity, which closed the loop rather nicely. The stock market is nothing more than a game of risk made up long ago, and it has long gotten out of hand. It is important to remember that *any* game will get out of hand once the understanding is lost that it is, in fact, a *game*. Just because we all are forced to be gamblers does not mean that the word stops applying to us, and you have to actually—

Me: I can tell you what I *have* to do, and that is restrain myself. You are the only person who I can think of who would think of nothing else at a time like this other than to try to advance your own ideas. You were probably hoping that I had lost enough money today to fall for your stupidity, but I would never let myself be that weak, even if I had lost everything. It really is—

Catty-Corner: Do you have a counterargument?

Me: I do not need one when your argument does not even make sense. You should be asking yourself that question since you do not even have an actual counterargument for the obvious thing that everyone already knows. I cannot believe that I let—

Catty-Corner: What is the obvious thing that everyone knows?

Me: I have already told you that. The fact that you have not listened to me at all is obvious, and you just admitted it, too. I had a bad enough day today that I should have just gone right inside without having stopped to talk to you at all. I knew it, but I still—

Catty-Corner: Are you leaving?

Me: Are you not able to tell that I am walking away?

ON GOODHOOD

Me: Afternoon, neighbor.

My Catty-Corner Neighbor: Good afternoon.

Me: Are you heading out somewhere or just getting back?

Catty-Corner: I am just getting home. I was able to do everything that I needed to get done this morning. How about yourself?

Me: I will not be going out at all today. I get so few days when I am not busy that I have to take full advantage of them. I usually feel busy just in trying to maximize my leisure, but that is just the way that it works, I suppose.

Catty-Corner: Do you have anything planned for your leisure today?

Me: I do not, and I am going to do my best not to. It does not make me feel particularly good about myself, of course, but I need one of those days.

Catty-Corner: What do you mean?

Me: I mean that I am tired, and I need my day of rest.

Catty-Corner: Why is that not good?

Me: It does not make me feel good.

Catty-Corner: Why not?

Me: Well, it makes me feel lazy, I suppose. I always try to be a good person and to do the right thing, but—

Catty-Corner: You try to be a *good* person?

Me: Of course. Everyone does, and I am sure that even you would, at the very least, *say* that you try to—

Catty-Corner: Of course not. I do not know a more—

Me: I should have known that if there was ever a bad path available then it would be the one for you. You really are a better definition of *vile* than the word itself. Every—

Catty-Corner: Have you ever worried about whether your wanting of goodhood makes you unworthy of it?

Me: What do you mean?

Catty-Corner: Well, wanting goodhood is an enviousness of it. It means that you are jealous of others who may have reached it, and *envy* and *jealousy* are, I think, usually regarded as sins. After all, how is purity able to withstand even the slightest smudge? Is it not true that aspiring to goodhood in any non-good way would be a path to it that would, instead, be nothing but a diversion directly from it? The truth is that if I ever wanted to achieve goodhood then the very last way that I would try to go about it would be to try to be a good person.

Me: Does that mean that your answer to things is to just not try? Being a good person seems difficult to you, so you do not even attempt it, and, instead, you laugh at those of us who do? All you do is smirk and—

Catty-Corner: Is it possible for a person to be good?

Me: Of course. That is just another one of your stupid, meaningless questions. I could list for you names upon names of people whom all the world knows to have been good.

Catty-Corner: I see.

Me: I hope that you do, but I know that you do not.

Catty-Corner: […]

Me: […]

Catty-Corner: Are you able to define goodhood for me?

Me: I should not have to.

Catty-Corner: Will you, though? *Can* you? Do you even have the—

Me: If you do not know what makes a person good then I am not sure that you can be helped, and the fact that you need goodhood defined is proof that it would be a wasted education, anyway.

Catty-Corner: You should be careful. Being wrathful will not bring you any closer to goodhood, and it may even—

Me: I am not going to take lessons from someone who does not know what he is talking about. You already admitted that you do not know what goodhood is, after all, but here we are with—

Catty-Corner: I never said that.

Me: You asked me to explain to you what a good person is.

Catty-Corner: Well, that does not mean that I do not have an idea myself. I was interested in the extent of your argument since the best strategy in the modern world is, after all, to allow your opponent to freely lay out his argument.

Me: It is easy to tell who a good person is because they are distinguishable from bad people, and if you cannot tell the former from the latter then it means that you are one of the latter. Is that simple enough for you?

Catty-Corner: Does that mean that good is the absence of bad? If I avoid doing bad then I become good? That does not sound right since it would mean that goodhood does not actually exist in the same way that cold does not. After all, if good is only the absence of bad then it is the same as cold being only the absence of heat. Do you, instead, mean that goodhood is the default? Everyone is inherently and always good until a transgression forces him off the path? Can you, in other words, tell me if it is true that goodhood has no characteristics of its own and is only defined by way of the things that it is not? I must admit that none of this sounds like goodhood to me.

Me: That is because none of it is. You are just twisting words and trying to turn them into something that they are not. Goodhood is obvious, and everyone would be able to point to it.

Catty-Corner: Then what exactly is it?

Me: If you are so smart then you should be able to tell me.

Catty-Corner: I will do that very thing. I would start by saying that the definition of goodhood seems to me to refer more to the motivations behind a particular act than to the act itself. People will, after all, call an act good in some cases while not necessarily so in others depending on the reasons behind it, and those motivations also tend to be viewed through the conditions surrounding them. You will, for example, sooner hear the poor man who gives away half his money called good than the rich man who gives away the same amount. If, however, the rich man gave away the same *percentage* as the poor man then such may give him a claim to an equal share of the prize. Goodhood, therefore, reveals itself to be a thing built upon both motivations and conditions, and such shows how an act itself can never be termed good since the actor is what makes the determination. Does that sound correct to you?

Me: I think that you are right in that the good of an act depends on the actor. There are, after all, many acts committed only for the *appearance* of goodhood, and it must be said that they fail in spirit that which they may follow to the letter.

Catty-Corner: What about the specific aspects of goodhood? Their dependence on motivation and condition makes them rather fluid, of course, but there does seem to be one characteristic that sticks to goodhood through all the many changes of time and place. This characteristic is best encapsulated by the word *selflessness*, and you will find that it is the most common symptom of alleged goodhood. In fact, fully selfless motives are often required before anyone will call his neighbor good, and a fully selfless condition is always the first thing pointed to whenever that neighbor is later defended as good. If these are to be—

Me: You are not saying anything important or special. Anyone would be able to tell you that selflessness is a major part of goodhood.

Catty-Corner: Well, if you know that goodhood is entwined with selflessness then would you still say that it is a possible thing for a person to be?

Me: Of course. It obviously does not—

Catty-Corner: Even with all the evidence before you?

Me: What do you mean?

Catty-Corner: Well, how would it be possible for a person to be selfless?

Me: People are selfless all the time. Just yesterday, for example, I let an older woman cut in front of me in line at the store. She had more things in her cart than I did, but I could tell that she was tired and was having a long day. I am not saying that I saved a life, but what I did was obviously selfless, so it is obviously possible for a person to be so.

Catty-Corner: Well, an act is only selfless if you do not take anything for yourself.

Me: Did you not hear the words that just went into your ears? You are acting like I charged the woman for cutting in front of me.

Catty-Corner: You did not charge her, but you used the experience to your credit. After all, that *selfless* interaction is being used by you right now to further the argument of your selflessness. You will often hear people say that doing good is its own reward, but that means that there *is* a reward, which means that whatever thing is being talked about cannot, by rule, be selfless, which means that it also cannot, by rule, have a claim to goodhood. The truth is that people do good so that they can feel good, and this makes goodhood forever foreign to them. No act can ever be good without consideration for its actor, and that actor can never be good due to his own motivations.

Me: This is all just your opinion, and it does not make any sense at all, anyway. All you are doing is saying that people are inherently bad, which is not even—

Catty-Corner: My point is that *existence* is inherently bad.

Me: What do you mean?

Catty-Corner: Well, a selfless state is a nonexistent one, and *that* is what I mean. The resting point of all things is selfishness. After all, every opportunity taken *must*, by rule, be seen as an opportunity denied elsewhere, and it is important to remember that you only exist because before your birth an incalculable number of other outcomes were denied that which you possess. One thing always exists because many others

194

do not. Existence is itself a selfish thing, and it has, therefore, very little to do with goodhood. To be is to be bad, and existence is an inherently less good thing than nonexistentence. Without—

Me: Are you saying that everyone is bad and will always be so?

Catty-Corner: Of course. This does not, however, mean that everything that *results* from you must be bad.

Me: What do you mean?

Catty-Corner: Well, all you must do is defy existence. Simply consider the things that feel natural to do, dismiss them, then reevaluate the situation. Take a meal, for example. Whenever you eat something then you are denying other things the opportunity of that same meal, which ignores whatever you may be doing to that meal itself, of course. It may, in other words, feel unavoidable to eat, but it is obviously not a good thing to do. If you actually want to do good then you must be willing to go in one direction while feeling as if everything is pulling you elsewhere, and you must also never let—

Me: This is the same thing that you have already been saying. I want to hear how goodhood is possible. You have said that both the act and actor cannot be good, so what does that leave?

Catty-Corner: The disembodied act can never be good, the inevitably-headed actor can never be good, but it is the *action* that has a chance. You can never achieve goodhood either in who you are or what you do, but the inspiring of good is within the reach of anyone and at any time. Take your allowing of the woman to cut you in line, for example. We have stripped away any claims to goodhood that you yourself may be able to have from the interaction, but it is important to remember that there are other factors.

Me: What do you mean?

Catty-Corner: Well, there were likely other shoppers around, after all, and they would have seen what you had done. This is the *action* that is separate from both the act and the actor. It is the *act* that is the thing that was done, it is the *actor* that was the doer, and it is the *action* that refers to the whole thing as witnessed from without. You may not have done anything definitively good by allowing the old woman in front of you, and you also may not be any closer to goodhood yourself, but you have forced into the world an example of the fact that the denying of the forces of existence is possible. The path to anywhere becomes far less obscure when guides are placed along the way, after all, and those who witness a good action become themselves able to repeat it, and it is even often true that the witnessing of a selfless action is a prerequisite for the witness's own belief in the thing's very possibility. The truth is that if you forget the act as well as yourself then goodhood becomes a much clearer thing, and it becomes obvious that good is something that must be done in the face of existence, not in accord with it.

Me: Is that all? There is not anything that you are keeping me from today, but I still do not like feeling as if I am wasting my time. You can keep talking if you want, though.

Catty-Corner: Well, the next part of my point is understanding shame to be the most powerful force for good that humanity has yet unearthed. It both sights the line and keeps it, and it—

Me: There it is. I was wondering how long it was going to take you today. The easiest way to counter every single one of your ideas is to just wait for you to reach the ridiculous part of your argument, and then it becomes easy to ignore you. We are obviously at that point now, so—

Catty-Corner: What do you mean?

Me: I mean that shame has nothing at all to do with goodhood, and everyone knows that. Shame is a thing that makes people feel bad about themselves, after all.

Catty-Corner: I see.

Me: The only things that you ever see are those that you are wanting to see. All you do is decide the way that you want things to be, and then you act as if that is all the argument that is needed. You are weak, stupid, and selfish, and the only question is how to order the adjectives.

Catty-Corner: I see.

Me: I will not see you.

ON SLAVERY

Me: Morning, neighbor.

My Catty-Corner Neighbor: Good morning.

Me: Are you staying home? I had, of course, assumed that you would, but I had also talked myself into hoping otherwise.

Catty-Corner: What do you mean?

Me: I mean the protest. Are you going?

Catty-Corner: What is being protested?

Me: The protest.

Catty-Corner: What do you mean?

Me: There is a protest going on downtown that everyone is getting together to protest. It has, in fact, been planned for a while.

Catty-Corner: What is being protested?

Me: By which side?

Catty-Corner: By the protesters that you are protesting.

Me: Why is *that* what you care about? All you want to do, I bet, is to find out which side I am against so that you can take it, and you do not care that things are obviously—

Catty-Corner: What is it that they are protesting?

Me: Well, that is the thing. They do not actually have any platform at all. Their whole worldview only concerns themselves, and they say that *they* are the ones who are actually being trodden upon. It is, of course, obvious that they are wrong, but they will not stop themselves, so we must do it for them. After all, I cannot think of anything more unamerican than allowing decidedly bad ideas to fester within the country.

Catty-Corner: I see.

Me: They do not even think about things at all, which is the worst part. They just see the path that looks as if it will favor them, and they leap upon it with stupid-strained hoots and simpleminded hollers. All you have to do is watch them waving their Confederate flags, and you will find yourself so—

Catty-Corner: Does your side wave the Union flag?

Me: What do you mean?

Catty-Corner: Well, does your side shame the past in the same way? Are you, in other words, so starry-eyed that you force the Stars and Stripes to strip for you? Is there, in fact, a—

Me: You are lucky that it is only me whom you are talking to.

Catty-Corner: What do you mean?

Me: I mean that if you go around trying to compare people to the Confederates then you are going to get yourself—

Catty-Corner: Well, who is it that everyone else thinks that we are like? The *North*?

Me: Of course.

Catty-Corner: In what way?

Me: Well, there is the obvious way of being on the same side against slavery. In fact, if you actually need me to make—

Catty-Corner: Americans today are not against slavery, though. Being complicit in the all-known is the same as supporting it, after all.

Me: I cannot believe that you are trying to make this argument. I really wish that you could actually listen to yourself speak sometime because it would be obvious to even you how much of—

Catty-Corner: Imagine a slave who is transported to our time from the Antebellum South.

Me: *Transported*? Do you mean by time travel? How would that happen?

Catty-Corner: It does not matter. What is important is to imagine him here.

Me: Did he come in a time machine, though? Was it built by someone? It would have to be mobile, I think, so it must have wheels and be—

Catty-Corner: Take any assumption of the words that you want. The plot of a story does not, after all, always have to be its most important element.

Me: Do not try to take your anger out on me. It is you who is the one forcing questions because he cannot come up with anything that makes sense, not me.

Catty-Corner: Imagine a slave who is transported to our time from the Antebellum South.

Me: I already did that.

Catty-Corner: Well, once the two of us had convinced him of where he has been transported to then what would happen?

Me: This is your argument, not mine, so I should not—

Catty-Corner: What would eventually happen, I think, is that he would ask us about our clothes. It is possible, after all, that we may have pulled him from a full, forced career in that industry, so it is likely that he would have some curiosity about that which he was familiar with. If you were to give him the shirt off your back so that he could start—

Me: Why would I do that?

Catty-Corner: What do you mean?

Me: Why would I give him the shirt off my back?

Catty-Corner: Because he needs it.

Me: I am wearing it, though. I would just go get him another one from my closet.

Catty-Corner: I see.

Me: That way, I would be handing him a clean one, too.

Catty-Corner: Well, once he is holding one of you extra shirts then what would happen?

Me: I just told you that this is your argument, not mine, so it does not make any sense for—

Catty-Corner: What would happen, I think, is that he would first be struck by the imaging on the shirt. There were not logos in his time, after all, so he would likely think that the word blazoned across the chest was your own name, and he would point to it, guess at its pronunciation, then point to you.

Me: Is that all?

Catty-Corner: Well, what would you tell him?

Me: I would correct him. I would explain to him that the logo refers to a specific brand.

Catty-Corner: Do you think that he would understand?

Me: Of course. Just because he is a slave does not mean that he is stupid, even though that is probably what you think.

Catty-Corner: Well, how about after he has had this opportunity to marvel at the way in which we brand ourselves? What would happen next?

Me: I already told you that I will not help you. I know that all you want to do is—

Catty-Corner: How about if he were to turn the shirt inside out?

Me: What do you mean?

Catty-Corner: Well, his attention would, I think, likely be attracted to the tag attached to the collar. It is like an extra piece of the shirt, after all, so he would begin examining it. He would see the several symbols and the odd, scientific words, but then there would be those all-prominent words in all-capital letters announcing where the shirt had come from. He would again, I think, assume the placement of those words to indicate your name, and it is likely that he would point to them, guess at their pronunciation, then point to you. When—

Me: This is the same thing that you said before. Whatever argument you are trying to make is so weak that you are repeating yourself.

Catty-Corner: Does that mean that you would explain the words on the tag to him just as you had done with the words on the front of the shirt? You would, in other words, tell the slave the truth?

Me: Of course.

Catty-Corner: What would you say?

Me: I would tell him that *MADE IN CHINA* is written on the tag because China is the place where the shirt came from.

Catty-Corner: Is that all?

Me: What do you mean?

Catty-Corner: Well, what if he marveled at the perfection of the shirt's stitching and declared that it was of such a quality that it could never have been done by the skill of man?

Me: I would explain to him that a lot of progress has taken place in the world since his time. We have all realized—

Catty-Corner: At what point in your listing of our progresses would you mention the one by which we transferred the yoke of slavery from him and his progeny to others and theirs? How long would it be before you tell the slave that your extra shirt was made by a slave? We have *progressed* from foolishly trying to hide slaves on the other side of the country to, instead, outsourcing them to the other side of the earth, which allows for the blissful equilibrium of us never having to see or hear them and they never being able to make themselves seen or heard. It does not matter which direction they attempt to run to us since all we have to do is simply spin the globe the other way, and they find themselves back where originally stationed. Fortuna's wheel famously had no favor, but tread's wheel has in its very design the purpose of bottoming the runner out, and we can even—

Me: What you are saying is deplorable. The way that you are trying to use the enslaved to your own advantage is disgusting, and you should be ashamed of yourself. They were people who actually lived, after all, not just tools for you to use as a way to improve your own life. Do you even have any idea how awful their lives were?

Catty-Corner: Do you have any idea that they have actually become *worse* since?

Me: What do you mean?

Catty-Corner: Well, it is not until hope goes unfulfilled that it becomes disappointed, after all. It is important to remember that we are talking about those who lived lives while having their bodies taken from them. They were themselves without ever being allowed to be themselves, and this denial was not just for the length of some agreed upon sacrifice but for their whole lives. There are certainly some in history who have individual claims to worse suffering, but there are not many plainer examples of those who—

Me: You are giving my argument. It was *me* who asked if you had any idea how bad their lives were, and it is *you* who is trying to trivialize their experiences so that you can make some personal point, which is—

Catty-Corner: My point is that hope should be regarded as the *only* possession that the slave could have ever actually had, and this hope could not have been a personal or even a descendent one. In the worst of conditions, after all, one instinctively takes heart in being able to make the slightest of progress either for himself or, at the very least, for his children, but what slave could have ever lied to himself so deeply? The truth is that not only is hope the only possession a slave could have had, but it would have been hope in its vaguest and most difficult to embrace sense. It would have been hope itself, and it would have—

Me: I am not going to listen to any more of this. If you actually think that I will stand by and let you try to use slavery for you own benefit then—

Catty-Corner: The point that I want to make is that slavery would have reduced the slave to not only mere hope but to even the most meager of hopes. It could be said that this hope would have been one of the few things that a slave could have never lost to his owner, and it was, instead, a removal reserved for posterity. After all, this most amorphous of hopes would likely have envisioned the *end* of slavery rather than just its transfiguration. I do not think that our transported slave would be impressed to discover that the ultimate surmounting of his suffering was but the unloading of it elsewhere. This is an individual who had his entire existence swallowed by his skin, after all, so is it not likely that he would find our modern world to actually be far *worse* than his hopefulness could have ever imagined? Is there anything—

Me: I have given you enough chances, I think. In fact, I have given you more than enough chances, and you have—

Catty-Corner: If we were, in fact, to actually tell our transported slave the truth then at what point in our telling of it would we expect him to take up arms against himself?

Me: That will be the last thing that I allow you to say to me today. You may think that you have planted some poisonous seed in me, but I can promise that I will forget this conversation as soon as I get to the protest. That is how weak your argument actually is. You have proven that all you want to do is attack me, anyway, so I do not even know why I would consider being—

Catty-Corner: The only way that any modern American could be said to be *against* slavery is that he stands so firmly atop it. Rationalize this fact however you will.

Me: I do not need to.

ON CAVES

Me: Evening, neighbor.

My Catty-Corner Neighbor: Good evening. I am glad that you said something. If you had not then I am not sure whether I would have noticed you.

Me: I could hardly see you myself. It must be the darkest night of the year.

Catty-Corner: It is certainly one of them. A new moon and cloud cover make an extremely unenlightening pair. Even they have their adherents, though, I suppose.

Me: It feels like we are in a cave. It really does. I thought that as soon as I walked outside. If there were not all the streetlights along the road then I do not think that we would be able to see at all.

Catty-Corner: There are a few with burned-out bulbs, too.

Me: I am surprised that it is not raining. I know that it was forecasted, and I thought that it would have started by now, but it must still be on its way.

Catty-Corner: Well, I suppose that that means that it is time to go inside. If only we were actually in a cave then we would not have to worry about it. We would, in fact, never have to worry about it, and the efficiency in replacing bulbs might be better, too.

Me: We would never see the sun, though.

Catty-Corner: Well, neither would we ever know of it.

Me: Hearing you say that does not surprise me at all. If there was anyone who would prefer to just stay seated and watching the shadows on the wall then it would be you. You probably even have some argument about how the warmth given off by the fire feels warmer than the sun's.

Catty-Corner: What fire?

Me: The fire that creates the shadows on the wall. How clear does a reference have to be before it gets through to you?

Catty-Corner: What shadows?

Me: Do you really not know the allegory? You are supposed to.

Catty-Corner: I am not sure.

Me: Well, then that makes it slightly better. I thought that you were being stupid, but if you really are just ignorant then it is, I suppose, less of a fault. Blind eyes are always far more morally defensible than unseeing ones, after all.

Catty-Corner: How does the allegory go?

Me: It starts by imagining a group of people who are kept chained in a cave for their whole lives while facing one wall. There is a large, ever-burning fire in the cave that throws shadows upon the wall faced by the prisoners, and these shadows result from objects that are passed between the fire and the wall. The prisoners cannot see these actual objects because of how they are chained, and they are only able to see the ensuing shadows, so they thus come to assume that the shadows are the physical objects themselves. The result is that the prisoners base their whole idea of the world on these things that are not actually so. Are you able to follow so far?

Catty-Corner: I think so.

Me: Are you sure? It is important, so you should make sure that you understand it

Catty-Corner: I am sure. How sure are you?

Me: Do not try to start anything in the middle of this. How could that even make sense, anyway? I am the one of us who knows the allegory, after all, so I am obviously sure.

Catty-Corner: What comes next?

Me: Well, imagine one of the prisoners being unchained and dragged up out of the cave. When in the sun then there—

Catty-Corner: What is he dragged by?

Me: What do you mean?

Catty-Corner: You said that one of the prisoners is dragged out of the cave. He was unchained, too. Who did both of those things?

Me: They are not part of the allegory. It is supposed to be a simple allegory that is also short, and you are already making it longer than it should have to be.

Catty-Corner: Was he awake when he was dragged, or does he just wake up outside?

Me: These things are not important at all. If you would just let me finish then you would understand the whole thing without having to ask any questions.

Catty-Corner: [...]

Me: The next thing that happens is that the former prisoner is able for the first time to see something other than the shadows upon the cave wall, and he sees the sun, and it at first causes—

Catty-Corner: That means that the unchaining and dragging *must* have happened while he was asleep. If he was awake, after all, then he would have already had several shocks before getting to that big one since the dragging itself would have been enlightening to him, I think. It is important to remember that he would have already seen in those few moments more than he had ever—

Me: How many times are you going to ruin things just as I am about to explain them? These things are not part of the story, so you should stop focusing on them. I was, of course, expecting you to find some way to misunderstand the allegory, but I did not think that we would not even be—

Catty-Corner: Will you tell me the rest of the story? I want to make sure that I am able to get back inside before it starts raining.

Me: Well, we are at the end of it, I suppose. The important part is realizing that the prisoner would see the world in the true light of the sun for the first time, and it would force him to change his opinions about everything. The other part to know is that if he were to go back into the cave to try to explain everything to his fellow prisoners then they would not believe him since they had not had his experience, and they would eventually regard him as crazy and dangerous, and it would form in their mind a hostility to any dragging out of the cave that might be attempted on them.

Catty-Corner: Is that all?

Me: It is the end of my summation. I should not even be having to do that much for you, though, and this is just one more of those times when I could have had this simple conversation with—

Catty-Corner: That is not what would happen, though.

Me: What do you mean?

Catty-Corner: Well, I do not think that the dragging part would happen. It seems believable to have one of the prisoners left unlocked, but it does not in the least bit seem feasible to include some force that drags him all the way out of the cave while at the same time shielding him from any sensations that could change his mind until the sun had its chance.

Me: Then what do you think would happen? You are going to say something stupid, I bet.

Catty-Corner: Well, I would probably say that the first moment when the prisoner realized that he was no long chained would be a moment of amazement for him in itself. If we remember his hitherto existence then it becomes clear to see that he would know nothing of his current situation other than the sudden realization that it was an unchained one succeeding a chained one, so he would inevitably think to flee, though he would hardly have a notion of what this word even means. He would seize his first opportunity, and he would run with all ability to whatever hallway in the cave system was nearest. His only guide would be the light of the fire, after all, which he would place at his back like a chasing beacon, and his path at every intersection would be determined by whichever way seemed to lead most directly from the light. He would eventually make a turn that finally hid the light of the fire from him completely, and he would become engulfed in darkness, and it is likely that he would here stop to rest and reflect. It is important to remember that it is during these moments that the prisoner would feel exhaustion for the first time, and it would likely scare him. He would also feel a pain in his knee, and he would reach down and discover blood as well as the fact that investigating the injury only made the sense of its hurt more acute. It is also at this point that he would be forced to realize that he had all along needed the light of the fire to be able to see at all. Many more similar considerations would force their way upon the prisoner, and he would have to conclude that he had acted hastily. It is important to remember that he does not know of the sun and that his running was only predicated on a momentary rejection of the fire as the symbol of his chains, so he does not know whether where he is now is, in fact, all there is, and it is likely that he would decide that he had a choice between striking off into further areas like his current one or attempting to return back to his place by the fire. It is obvious which he would choose, and he would scramble back the way that he had come while trying to remember as many of the turns as possible, and it is entirely possible that this is the way in which his life would end, and his last moments would be spent in pitying himself for having forsaken that lost touchstone, which, though perhaps planted on sand, had, at the very least, seemed to be on actual ground. If, however, the prisoner was able to make his way back to the fire then the first thing that he would do would be to sneak back to his spot and quietly snap shut about him the locks of his chains. There would likely be a few tense moments for him while wondering whether anyone had witnessed either his escape or return, but once assured of his safety then he would rejoice in it, and he would regard it as a miracle that he had been able to recover himself to the fire. His former illusion of the fire and shadows on the wall being existence itself has been shattered, of course, but this is a secret that he is not forced to reveal, and he does, in fact, determine to keep it safe within himself, and this will keep him safe in turn. It is likely that his private moments in later years would return to his harrowing ordeal in the wilderness, and it is likely that he would be able to reason such things as the fact that he had never first bled until he had first stumbled and that he had never first become tired until he had first run. Is it not likely, in other words, that he would reach the conclusion that even a lie is preferable to nothing at all?

Me: [...]

Catty-Corner: [...]

Me: Is that all?

Catty-Corner: Well, there is probably a lot more, but—

Me: Well, it will all have to be saved for another day. I really do think that the rain is going to begin at any minute.

Catty-Corner: It is hard to tell.

Me: I am heading inside. I am not going to take a chance of getting caught in it.

Catty-Corner: What did you think of my allegory?

Me: It was a very nice story. It was a little long, though, so there were a few parts of it that I missed.

Catty-Corner: What were the parts that you missed?

Me: I will have to tell you another time. I am going back inside, and you should, too.

ON OPENMINDEDNESS

Me: Morning, neighbor.

My Catty-Corner Neighbor: Good morning. You are in plenty of time to be able to see the sunrise.

Me: I am actually going to miss it since I am on my way out.

Catty-Corner: Where to?

Me: I am trying something new today. I have had a number of people trying to get me into this new pre-breakfast fad for a while, and I am finally giving in. I am on my way to meet a few friends at a new restaurant that specializes in it.

Catty-Corner: I have not heard of it.

Me: Well, you will soon. Everyone thinks that it is about to be the next big thing. I am trying to get in before it blows up.

Catty-Corner: What is it?

Me: It is just another meal added in before breakfast. It is from the Middle East, I think, and called *Suhoor* or something like that, and it is a big health thing. The time between dinner and breakfast is the unhealthiest of all for most people since no one really eats during those times, and this means that your body is being forced to operate at a loss during all those hours every single night. It sounds like it would be best for our health if we were able to eat continuously, but that is not a realistic ideal, so Suhoor is the first step.

Catty-Corner: I see. What does it consist of?

Me: I am not sure. It is a return-to-nature thing, so all the dishes were ones that I had not heard of. There are probably going to be all sorts of ingredients that I have never even tried before, too.

Catty-Corner: The menu will hopefully have pictures.

Me: It will not matter if it does not. I am willing to try something new, which is one of the biggest differences between you and me, and I am able to stomach what my stomach may not be asking for. Most people are not as openminded as I am, and they are never willing to—

Catty-Corner: You are not openminded.

Me: My openmindedness is proved every single time that I talk to you, and I am able to call myself it because I never—

Catty-Corner: That is how I know that it is not true. You cannot say that you are openminded while being so.

Me: That does not make any sense at all. I would be the one to know if I was openminded, after all, since I know myself best, and I know that I am so. In fact, it is you who is the closeminded one, and you are probably even the most closedminded person whom I have ever known. You always have your mind set on something and then never change it, even when I point out how stupid you are.

Catty-Corner: Can we debate the meaning of openmindedness?

Me: What do you mean?

Catty-Corner: Well, it should be obvious that you will be unable. You have, after all, stated the bounds of openmindedness and thus closed them, which is not a very *openminded* thing to do. You have defined something as well as applied it to yourself, and the latter is as dangerous as the former is foolish. Once it is you, after all, then a thing can only ever be removed painfully, which means that it is far more likely to merely be covered.

Me: You are overthinking things. This is something that is simple and obvious, and I am not sure why you are having so much trouble with it. I want—

Catty-Corner: My point is that once you call yourself openminded then the true fullness of your closedmindedness begins. It is, for example, like a person trying to speak to his own muteness since the very action belies the whole act. Any concrete claim of openmindedness is cemented proof of the opposite, and no actually *open* mind would ever even think of declaring itself as such.

Me: […]

Catty-Corner: Are you leaving?

Me: Of course. I told you that I was in a hurry to meet my friends for something new that I am trying, and you made everything about yourself in the same way that you always do. I am probably going to be late now, too, and I bet that you do not even care. I know that I am right, so I do not even know why I let you waste my time.

Catty-Corner: Can you share your counterargument with me so that I can be right, too? It would be rather *closehearted* to force me to persist in wrongness, after all.

Me: I do not have time. I am late for my plans.

Catty-Corner: I see. Well, I await your counterargument. What time will you be back?

Me: I have not decided. I may see you tomorrow, but I do not want to think about it right now.

ON TOLERANCE

Me: Morning, neighbor.

My Catty-Corner Neighbor: Good morning.

Me: It certainly is a good morning, and it is, in fact, a glorious one. There is not a single cloud in the sky, but the sun seems to have noticed the absence and will, therefore, not be getting too warm, so we will be in for a perfect day. It is enough to make me wish that I was not in a hurry.

Catty-Corner: You are in a hurry?

Me: Of course. I am always in a hurry. If one is not always on the move then one gets left behind.

Catty-Corner: I see.

Me: […]

Catty-Corner: […]

Me: Well, I suppose that I will see you this evening or hopefully tomorrow. I can, after all, have my morning reflection anywhere just as well as here, and I will, in fact, soon be without you distracting me every—

Catty-Corner: Your *mooring deflection*?

Me: My *morning reflection.*

Catty-Corner: I see.

Me: […]

Catty-Corner: What is it that you reflect on?

Me: Well, it depends on what I want to think about. If I am reflecting in the morning, for example, then I usually think about the rest of my day. If I am around you, however, then the decision is taken from me, and I am forced to reflect on how it is possible for the intolerant to exist on days like the glorious one that we have today.

Catty-Corner: The intolerant are the way that they are because there is no other way for them to be, and there is, therefore, no mystery at all.

Me: What do you mean?

Catty-Corner: Well, tolerance depends on creed. Take, for example, the relationship between a Christian and a heathen. The Christian, of course, may not approve of the heathen, but within his creed is the ability to accept that other, and the Christian, in fact, knows that the path of the world is such that the other is inevitable. The Christian regards the self as a sinner, and he is, therefore, able to be tolerant.

Me: […]

Catty-Corner: Now take the example of the relationship between a scientist and a luddite. The scientist, of course, may not approve of the luddite, but within his creed is the ability to accept that other, and the scientist, in fact, knows that the path of the world is such that the other is inevitable. The scientist regards the self skeptically, and he is, therefore, able to be tolerant.

Me: I have, I think, heard enough to know what—

Catty-Corner: Now take the example of the relationship between a sociologist and a dissenter. The sociologist, of course, will not approve of the dissenter, and within his creed is the necessity of reform, so any *true* sociologist, in fact, will find within himself the inability to tolerate that other at all. The sociologist stands upon statistics, and it is for this reason that he must be protective of them, which means that any dissenter becomes an unacceptable disrupter. The sociologist regards himself as a direct interpreter of reality, and he is not, therefore, able to be tolerant.

Me: […]

Catty-Corner: It is also important to remember that a—

Me: I do not want to hear anything more from you. I did not speak because I was trying to return to my reflection, which should, I think, have been obvious to even you. If I wanted to hear about how stupid—

Catty-Corner: My point is that tolerance is not a matter of choice but rather the *result* of choice. To choose narrowness is, after all, narrowing, and those whose justifications extend merely to immediate surroundings will soon find—

Me: I am leaving, and if you do not get out of my way then I will hit you. You are the most intolerant person that I have ever met, and you are one of the stupidest, too. The fact that you can be so mean proves—

Catty-Corner: Will you share your counterargument with me before you go? If I can then I will choose to be tolerant of it.

Me: I know that you cannot promise that because it is not something that you could ever be.

Catty-Corner: I see.

Me: [...]

Catty-Corner: The truth is that tolerance seems to be slipping away from the world because it is, in fact, doing that very thing. When one's rock is Christianity then tolerance is possible, and when one's rock is science then tolerance is possible, but when one's rock is sociology then tolerance is impossible, and the statistic-stander will always be required to play an unending game of king of the hill.

Me: Get out of my way.

ON LOVE

Me: Evening, neighbor.

My Catty-Corner Neighbor: Good evening. It is good to see you.

Me: Well, I cannot say the same. It is obvious that you have something that you want to ask me, which means that it will be something that no one would ever want to hear.

Catty-Corner: […]

Me: Do you want to tell me that I am wrong?

Catty-Corner: Can I make my point before you do so?

Me: […]

Catty-Corner: All I wanted to ask is whether the extreme of concern is love since I have been—

Me: Love is obviously the extreme of concern. Everyone knows that.

Catty-Corner: Well, if that is true then is hate the other extreme? It would, I think, have to—

Me: Of course not. Hate means hating someone.

Catty-Corner: I see.

Me: Well, I see that you are embarrassed by how easy your stupid question was for me, so you want to make it seem—

Catty-Corner: Is hate a form of concern?

Me: Of course not. Everyone knows—

Catty-Corner: Does that mean that hate is a form of indifference?

Me: Of course not. To hate means to hate, after all.

Catty-Corner: Well, if hate is not a form of indifference then it must be a form of concern since those are the two options. Hate either fits within the side of feeling that concerns itself with the object, which includes such feelings as love, friendship, and courage, or it fits within the side of feeling that does not concern itself with the object, which includes such feelings as lust, loyalty, and bravery.

Me: What you are saying does not make any sense at all. Everyone knows that hating someone means that you do not care about him, which is—

Catty-Corner: The truth is that one must first care to ever hate, and the word for the feeling that represents that extreme of indifference is *prejudice*, which is the opposite of hate in the same way that lust is the opposite of love. The feelings of hate and love are, in other words, antipodes on the globe of concern in the same way that prejudice and lust are antipodes on the globe of indifference.

Me: You are *still* not making any sense, and it is obvious, I think, that you have not been trying to. You said that you had a point that you wanted to make, but, instead, you just wanted to ramble and hope that I would listen for as long as—

Catty-Corner: My point is that those who pat their own backs for not allowing themselves to hate are the same who push themselves into being ineligible for love. After all, to deny the extreme that would be required to reach one pole is to deny the presence of an amount that could ever reach the other. It is important to remember that one singes oneself at one's own peril, and to be unable to hate is to be incapable of love.

Me: Well, I am one of those who would say that he never hates. Does that mean that you think that I can never love? Because if—

Catty-Corner: Of course. That is what I have been trying to tell you this whole time.

Me: If that is the point that you have wanted to make all along then I hate myself for allowing you to say it. I should have walked inside then rather than now, and it would have saved me from the—

Catty-Corner: The truth is that a capability of being in love goes hand in hand with the same for hate in the same way that the same for lust goes hand in hand with the same for prejudice. In other words, the *love* for that which one does not care about is, instead, *lust* in the same way that the *hate* for that which one does not care about is, instead, *prejudice*. The length of range is a choice, and if you decide to place yourself safely beyond the reach of others then you should not be surprised when they are unable to touch you from any direction, no matter the intention or means. A self-centering life, after all, will be a self-centered one, and its own walls often stretch out of its sight and to the—

Me: What you are saying is one of the most hateful things that I have ever heard. *Hate-filled*, I think, would actually be the better—

Catty-Corner: Well, will you share your counterargument with—

Me: I would not share anything with you, even if it was important, which everything that you say is not. I am going back—

Catty-Corner: The last thing that I want to—

Me: I already did the last thing.

ON LOVING

Me: Afternoon, neighbor.

My Catty-Corner Neighbor: Good afternoon. It is good to see you. Were you able to find some way to take advantage of the dreary morning that we had?

Me: I did that very thing, and I hope that you were able to do it, too. There was nothing on my schedule that forced me to get up early, so I was able to sleep in, and the sound of rain on the roof when I awoke was so peaceful that I stayed in bed for several hours listening to it. In fact, it was so peaceful that I fell back asleep, and I am, therefore, more refreshed today than I am used to being. I am so well-rested that it feels as if I am still in my dream.

Catty-Corner: [...]

Me: It is perfect, I think, when days are like this. Everyone always says that they prefer only the sun, but I like it when a day blossoms. To have it rain in the early morning then become sunny by noon is a special type of setting, and it makes the day feel as if it is a stage that has been cleaned and prepared for the performance of our lives.

Catty-Corner: Well, I am glad that you had such a great morning. After all, there is not a—

Me: That morning of mine was, in fact, so great that I am already starting to feel nostalgic for it. I was so curled into my comforter that it felt like a second, supporting skin, and I was snug enough that my mind swam. It did, in fact, bring back to me memories of a similar morning from long ago.

Catty-Corner: What do you mean?

Me: Well, I am not sure whether I should tell you. It could get me into trouble, after all.

Catty-Corner: […]

Me: I can tell you, I suppose. There is, after all, hardly anyone that I have to worry about you telling it to, and it will, therefore, be safe with you, even though it is not actually a secret.

Catty-Corner: […]

Me: That morning from long ago was back when I was young and living downtown. To remember it feels like remembering the actions of another person, and it was a time in my life when I was staying out late every night, which means that it was the opposite of my life now. There are, I think, two types of livable life, and they are most distinguished by the people that you meet while living each of them. After all, people must sleep at *some* time, so the choice between day or night means that one only meets like types, and he will, in fact, only reinforce his original choice by way of repeated outcome. It is, therefore, so very difficult to change one's lifestyle, no matter what it might be.

Catty-Corner: Were you thinking these things during that morning long ago?

Me: Of course not. I was merely commenting a little on life, but doing so, I suppose, may have brought me out a little too far beyond you.

Catty-Corner: […]

Me: That morning from long ago was one like today, and there was the same type of rain that made it perfect to stay in bed. I did not have any plans that day, either, so I stayed in bed all morning then, too. The only difference, however, was that I was not alone in my bed during that morning long ago.

Catty-Corner: I see.

Me: Well, I know that you do not because I was not with the one whom you are thinking of. This was, after all, years ago, and it was back when I was living downtown.

Catty-Corner: What do you mean?

Me: I mean that the one whom I was with then was my *one who got away*. That is, at the very least, the term by which I have always found myself unable to forget her by. I am, of course, with my true one now, but I had not yet even met her at the time when—

Catty-Corner: What is a *true one*?

Me: […]

Catty-Corner: What is a *true*—

Me: Do you really not know what it is? If you actually do not then I will feel sorry for you, but I am sure that—

Catty-Corner: Well, will you tell me what it is? That way, I will no longer be in my sorry state.

Me: Your true one is the person whom you are supposed to be with. It refers to each person's destined counterpart, and it means—

Catty-Corner: Does that mean that *everyone* has a *true one*? There is, in other words, someone out there who is a match for every person?

Me: Of course. That is what I just—

Catty-Corner: What about those who die in youth? Do they, therefore, leave behind one who will no longer have a match, or is it—

235

Me: That is not what we are talking about at all. We are talking about love, not anything to do with death.

Catty-Corner: I see.

Me: I really do feel sorry for you. Anyone else would know what I was talking about, and it must be because of the fact that you have never been touched by the feeling.

Catty-Corner: Does that mean that I do not have a *true one*?

Me: Of course not. Everyone has a true one, which is what I just said.

Catty-Corner: Does that mean that I am the *true one* of my *true one*?

Me: Of course. That is a stupid question because it could have been assumed from already knowing the other as your true one.

Catty-Corner: Well, if a *true one* never meets its *true one* then do they each still remain the other's *true one*?

Me: [...]

Catty-Corner: Take me, for example. You said that you feel sorry for me because I have never felt the feeling, which must mean—

Me: That is true, and no one would ever argue against it.

Catty-Corner: Well, does my failure not doom my *true one*? I am, after all, her *true one*, too, so if my poor heart never allows me to be led to her then is her even poorer heart not left forever alone? What makes unrealized *true ones* remain *true ones*?

Me: None of this is important at all. I told you that everyone has a true one, which is what—

Catty-Corner: The truth is that you believe in a *true one* because it provides for you a proof that you are a *perfect one*. To believe in fate is, after all, to believe in faultlessness since it must mean that each past hug and snub was correctly acted to the appropriate gauge, and belief in a *true one* is, therefore, due to a desire to rationalize *past ones*.

Me: I have already told you—

Catty-Corner: How, after all, do you know that your *one that got away* is not, in fact, actually your *true one*?

Me: […]

Catty-Corner: How do you know that your *one that got*—

Me: Because everything that was then is now more, which is what anyone would be able—

Catty-Corner: Well, if compatibility is, in fact, a ladder then how do you know that you are settled on its highest rung? A gradational founding is, after all, a mobile one, and the truth is that if true love did, in fact, exist then no one would ever be able to bear loving anyone else.

Me: [...]

Catty-Corner: Will you share your counterargument with me for how you—

Me: I will not. I know what I know, and I know that it is true. You have not made any real argument, either, so I do not need a counterargument, anyway.

ON AFFECTION

Me: Afternoon, neighbor.

My Catty-Corner Neighbor: Good afternoon. How was your morning?

Me: It was wonderful. We all had a big breakfast together out on the back patio, and we have been talking about what to go out and do this evening. How about your morning?

Catty-Corner: Mine was good, but it was not as full, though. Do you have time to continue our conversation from yesterday?

Me: Of course not. How can you even ask that when you should know what my answer would be? I told you how good my day has been so far, after all.

Catty-Corner: Well, I thought that there—

Me: We were not even having a *conversation*, anyway. All you were doing was insulting me, so why would I want to continue that? I cannot believe that you would try to ruin my morning after knowing how—

Catty-Corner: The last thing that we had talked about was you making a point.

Me: That is not important at all. The only thing that will happen is that I will make my point, and you will belittle it, and then you will act like you have achieved something. It will be the same as every other day, so why would I do it when I know that the result is going to make me upset?

Catty-Corner: If I can just make my final point then I think that you will—

Me: Did you not listen to what I just said? I do not care. If whatever it is that you have to say is so important then you would be able to say it in a way that did not insult me. Whatever I think about something does not affect you, anyway, so I do not know why you cannot just let—

Catty-Corner: You used *affect* wrong.

Me: Do you think that it is supposed to be *effect*? You must be affected with an infecting effect. You may not be able to understand that joke, so I will just tell you that you must be one of the stupidest people to have ever even attempted speech. Not knowing the difference between *affect* and *effect* is—

Catty-Corner: Is it worse than not actually knowing either?

Me: What do you mean?

Catty-Corner: Well, is a confused distinction any worse than distinct confusion?

Me: You can keep trying to not make sense as a way of getting under my skin, but I can promise that it will not work. It is your only tactic, so I know that it is your only hope. I really do feel sorry for you. I cannot imagine how empty you must be to feel as if you have to fill yourself up by attacking me. I know that it must be hard for you to accept—

Catty-Corner: You are not answering my question. If you would just stick to the point for once then you—

Me: You want *me* to stick to the point? You are the one who only ever cares about your own arguments and only listens to people so that you can find some unimportant way to call them wrong. It would be easy for me to list more than ten times when you have strayed so far from the point as to be nonsensical, and it is something that I always point out at the time, too. It happened twice yesterday, in fact, and there was the time last weekend when you tried to convince me of—

Catty-Corner: Are these ramblings on point?

Me: They are on the point of your stupidity, which seems to always be the eventual topic of most of—

Catty-Corner: The point was your usage of *affect*. You used it in a way that showed your ignorance of it.

Me: That is not true, and your lying shows a lot about you. Your entire method is to mock then remember yourself as having been the mocked. It was me who was making fun of you for not knowing the word, after all, so I obviously know it myself.

Catty-Corner: What you said was that what you think does not *affect* me, which is incorrect.

Me: I am glad to hear you actually admit that because it perfectly summarizes how selfish of a person you are. It was something that I already knew, of course, but hearing you say out loud that you think that I am not allowed to think whatever I want is an—

Catty-Corner: Have you ever been to Europe?

Me: What do you mean?

Catty-Corner: Has your physical being ever physically existed in the place referred—

Me: I am going to leave if you talk to me like that. This is not what I want to be doing with my time, anyway.

Catty-Corner: Have you ever been to Europe?

Me: Of course not.

Catty-Corner: Well, imagine yourself traveling there and finding—

Me: I would never do that. I hate—

Catty-Corner: That is not important at all. This is a hypothetical situation, after all, and taking issue with being mischaracterized in such is evidence of one's not understanding the nature of it.

Me: Why is Europe important?

Catty-Corner: Well, why would you never choose to go there?

Me: I have heard too many bad things. Everyone says that the people are rude.

Catty-Corner: Does that mean that they *affect* you?

Me: Of course not. I have never meet any of them, and they have never meet me.

Catty-Corner: Well, if they do not *affect* you then how can you explain the *effect* that they have on you? How, in other words, could they be able to have a formed opinion of you for you to get annoyed by upon arrival?

Me: Well, they are not the type of people over there who actually—

Catty-Corner: Let us try an example that is further removed from your prejudices. How about if—

Me: The only one here who is prejudiced is you, and it is against me, and it is obvious. Your only point is that you like Europe, I bet, and you want to try—

Catty-Corner: My point is that you *affect* everyone far more often than you do no one. It is important to remember that the expected behavior of a person is based on the past behavior of people, and normalcy is the derivative of former whim just as the ordinary is the product of the repeated extraordinary. Do changes in people not, after all, change people? How, for example, would those Europeans be able to have a preconceived notion of you other than by forming it based on previous Americans? In other words, those previous Americans *must* be said to have affected you, even though they may have never intended to, and they may, in fact, have even shared your absurd notion of insulated isolation. The truth is that affection always transcends intention, and it is obvious that there is—

Me: I am going to go return to my morning. If you are wondering then I will let you know that you have not changed my mind in the slightest. I can think whatever I want to in my own head, after all, and it is not your business or anyone else's.

Catty-Corner: Well, you may be able to think whatever you want, but the notion that such will never influence anyone but yourself is selfishness in its stupidest form. It is, in other words, an obvious fiction that you tell yourself so that you can retain all your fictions, and you want to feel free from *effect* so that you will not feel guilty about never being concerned about your *affect*. It is important to remember that all things eventually affect all others, and you are at all times under the effect of a world caused by affect. After all, do you not determine your personhood by first distinguishing yourself from—

Me: Why will you not just leave me alone? I know that you can tell that I—

Catty-Corner: Because there is no such thing. That has been my point this whole—

Me: Thank you for saying that. I was going to feel bad about walking away from you, but hearing such a stupid parting from you makes me feel a lot better about it.

ON APPEARANCES

Me: Evening, neighbor.

My Catty-Corner Neighbor: Good evening. It is good to see you, and it does, in fact, look like you have seen something good, too.

Me: Is it that obvious? I left the theater less than an hour ago. Do I smell like popcorn?

Catty-Corner: I may perhaps be getting a whiff of it. Your face, however, has the glow of one who has been recently enlightened by a screen, and it is a full tint.

Me: […]

Catty-Corner: […]

Me: Was that comment supposed to mean something mean?

Catty-Corner: I do not think so.

Me: Well, that is good to hear.

Catty-Corner: […]

Me: […]

Catty-Corner: What was the movie that you went to see?

Me: Do you really not know?

Catty-Corner: […]

Me: I went to go see the one that everyone is going to see. Everyone has been talking about it since back when it was first announced, after all, which I am sure that you heard. It has been starting to receive a lot of award buzz, too.

Catty-Corner: I know it well.

Me: If that is true then have you seen it, and what did you think of it? I thought that it was even a lot better than most people were expecting it to be.

Catty-Corner: I watched each of the trailers upon their release, and I have read a few reviews, too. It does not look like a movie that I would enjoy.

Me: Well, just because you know that you will not like it does not mean that it is bad. It was intended for everyone, so you should give it a chance.

Catty-Corner: I see.

Me: I know that you are a fan of the series, too, so there is not any reason why you should not want to see it. If the problem is that the price of a movie ticket is too high then there are all sorts of ways to watch it for free. What is important is that you watch it.

Catty-Corner: […]

Me: If you were not so judgmental all the time then you would know a lot more about the world than you actually do. You decide that you are going to hate things before knowing about them, which is why you do not know anything at all, and you are exactly the opposite of me. I am, after all, careful to never judge a book by its cover while always investigating things to their—

Catty-Corner: You do not judge the cover of books?

Me: Well, if a cover is poorly designed then I will, of course, judge it harshly. I will not, however, judge the book by it.

Catty-Corner: What about the *back* covers? Do you judge books by them? I find that these aspects are those that every book is judged upon, and they are, in fact, the very deciders of readership.

Me: That is not what we are talking about at all. You are just trying to make some stupid point that will not make any sense, anyway, which is what you always do. I was planning on coming home and rewatching all the movies in the series, so I think that I will go and—

Catty-Corner: The truth is that to not judge books by their covers is itself a judgement. The choice to ignore is, after all, a choice, and it is important to remember that a predetermination is still a determination.

Me: The only thing that is important right now is the movie that I just saw since I just saw it, so if there is anything about the series that you think is important to say then you should say it while it is on my mind.

Catty-Corner: [...]

Me: Well, not answering is enough of an answer, and I suppose that I should not be surprised to find out that your complaints about the series amount to not even being able to say them when the time comes. I cannot believe that you—

Catty-Corner: You can go inside, start your movies, and pat yourself on the back for your lack of prejudice, but such will still remain a prejudice, and the truth is that you can say whatever you like, but the *appearance* of a thing is that which most decides its fate, and this fact is, in fact, truer today than it has ever been before.

Me: The last thing that I am going to say before I close the door is that you are the perfect example of why movies are necessary. You only want to tear down, so we need to have those who build up.

ON REPRESENTATION

Me: Afternoon, neighbor.

My Catty-Corner Neighbor: Good afternoon.

Me: […]

Catty-Corner: […]

Me: I may regret asking this, but I have an extra ticket to the movie that I am on my way to see. Would you like to join me? If you want then you can ride with me, and the movie is—

Catty-Corner: Thank you, but I do not think so.

Me: […]

Catty-Corner: […]

Me: I am not asking for you to pay me. It would be a free ticket.

Catty-Corner: Well, I am thankful but not interested.

Me: […]

Catty-Corner: I do not want to see any of the movies that are out. They are, I think, only—

Me: I see.

Catty-Corner: What do you mean?

Me: Well, it is obvious that you are afraid of what you might see, and it is a phobia of learning. Anyone, after all, would always want to see a movie, particularly if it is free, so if you do not want to see it then you must be against it.

Catty-Corner: [...]

Me: You know that movies are no longer just entertainment but that they now have messages, and it bothers you that others are finally being represented in art, which shows that you—

Catty-Corner: Others are now being represented?

Me: Of course.

Catty-Corner: Who are these newly represented?

Me: Well, they include just about everyone. Are you really going to insult all—

Catty-Corner: I did not say anything about them. I asked who they are.

Me: Well, the newly represented are all those who have not been previously represented.

Catty-Corner: […]

Me: […]

Catty-Corner: Well, does that mean that every individual's first representation is always a triumph? Each of us, after all, begins life after not having previously lived, so we are, therefore, all unrepresented until—

Me: That is not what we are talking about at all. We are talking about new *types* of people being represented, not any actual person.

Catty-Corner: I see.

Me: Everyone knows what I am talking about, so it is obvious that you are just trying to be—

Catty-Corner: The truth is that those who feel as if they are just now being represented are actually those who have historically received more attention than any other group. After all, the free-lovingly revelous fill as many pages as do the duties of kings, and those who serve the heights of their own callings have been set apart since the very beginning of time. In fact, there is not a more—

Me: You are not making any sense at all. Everyone knows that those who are now being represented are those who have never been represented before. In fact, all you have to do is ask them, and they will tell you that they represent the historically unrepresented.

Catty-Corner: Well, what if they are wrong? After all, it could be that they were told—

Me: That cannot, by rule, be true. It is *their* representation, after all, so they would know if it has happened before.

Catty-Corner: I see.

Me: If they really were already represented then where are those representations? I want you to answer that since I know that you will not actually have—

Catty-Corner: Well, you may not like those actual representations.

Me: […]

Catty-Corner: […]

Me: If I do not like them then it will be because of the fact that they are wrong.

Catty-Corner: […]

Me: You do not, I bet, even have anything to actually say, and you were so sure that I would not challenge you that you did not expect to have—

Catty-Corner: Our past representations are those who were portrayed as living lives like ours. They are often mentioned as part of large, unending parties that feature more pleasure than a pit full of the feeling. They are often mentioned as adroit users of language for their own benefit, which often only extends to the purposes of their merrymaking. They are often mentioned in the ear of the downtrodden while in the pocket of the tread. They are often mentioned as slaves to chaos while conducting acts of enslavement. They are often mentioned as mockers of moral codes while coded blockers of—

Me: Well, who are they? You have not said their names, so I cannot know whether—

Catty-Corner: Some of them, I suppose, have been given special names, but they have for a millennium simply been referred to as *demons*, and the proof that we are their—

Me: I do not think that I will ever let you speak to me again.

ON SOCIALISM

Me: Evening, neighbor.

My Catty-Corner Neighbor: Good evening. It is good to see you. I have been wanting to ask you all day whether—

Me: Do not come any closer. I could see through my window that you were waiting to ambush me as soon as I was outside. I would not have even come out if I did not have to, but there was no—

Catty-Corner: All I wanted to ask is whether you have played the new game that everyone is talking about. It has, after all, been—

Me: What new game? Is it fun?

Catty-Corner: It is a game that shows where you are on the political spectrum, so it *might* be fun for some, but for—

Me: What do you mean?

Catty-Corner: Well, the game has you answer questions, and then it tells you where you are politically. That way, people can learn about themselves, and it is, in fact, only one question, so the game can be—

Me: It is only *one* question?

Catty-Corner: One is all that is needed.

Me: [...]

Catty-Corner: How about if I ask you the question?

Me: I already know where I am politically.

Catty-Corner: [...]

Me: If it is actually just one question then ask it or leave me alone. Those are your two options, so you should not act like—

Catty-Corner: The question is a short one, and it concerns socialism and its relationship with the United States. You are supposed to consider whether—

Me: Socialism is the future of the country, and everyone knows that. It is what we need, and most people want it, too.

Catty-Corner: [...]

Me: Well, it is obvious that your question comes from the other side. Does that mean that the correct answer should have been that the country will never be socialist?

Catty-Corner: [...]

Me: Well, which of the two is it? I have given both answers, so you cannot be angry that I have—

Catty-Corner: Both answers are the same as far as their relation to the question.

Me: What do you mean?

Catty-Corner: Well, your first answer classes you as leaning *decidedly stupid*, and the second does the same thing. After all, there is not a more obvious—

Me: If anyone is stupid then it is you, not me. After all, you are the one who thinks that he can know anything about someone from just one question, and I gave you the two answers, anyway, so they cannot *both* be wrong.

Catty-Corner: I see.

Me: Well, it is obvious that your game has not been the fun that you were expecting it to be, so maybe you should—

Catty-Corner: The truth is that the United States has been socialist for as long as those states have been united.

Me: What do you mean?

Catty-Corner: I mean that the country's first major act was a socialist one. The Hamiltonian Compromise, after all, involved the federal assumption of state debts, and nowhere in the foundations of our government is this federal function detailed. The claim underlying the Compromise was, therefore, a *societal* one, and it is important to remember—

Me: What you are saying is not true. Everyone knows that socialism was invented by Marx, and he was—

Catty-Corner: The truth is that socialism would not be any more confusing to a person of the distant past than would be the idea of either democracy or aristocracy. Socialism, after all, simply refers to governmental proactivity, which is counter to its natural state of reactivity. Marx, instead, invented *Marxism*, which simply refers to the perversion of socialism into a servility to the self. Marxism, in other words, is nothing more than a cloak for the misanthrope and a playbook for the antisocial, and it is a moral code that rationalizes the usage of others through election by suffering. It is both sword and shield for the selfish, and it is a placebo for the pseudo intellectual. It is a chain for the body while opium for the mind, and it is a faith for the outwardly faithless. The greatest trick that Marx ever pulled was in railing against religion while slowly registering his own.

Me: […]

Catty-Corner: Socialism is a tool of government rather than a type, and it is for this reason that it should never be either ordained or disdained. If society is failing then socialism needs enacting in the same way that if society is succeeding then socialism needs repealing. *True* socialism, after all, was invented by those who realized that feudalism was not wholly bad, and its purpose was to ensure that whatever government that capitalism created would not be wholly bad. *Socialism* is, therefore, a tool of government while *Communism* is the term for its application into a type, and *Marxism* is its mangling into a belief system.

Me: […]

Catty-Corner: It is also important to remember that effect should always be more decisive than image, and we do, after all, claim to hate kings while our courtrooms act as miniature monarchies, so I do not see why—

Me: You need to move so that I can get my car out.

ON DEMOCRACY

Me: Afternoon, neighbor.

My Catty-Corner Neighbor: Good afternoon.

Me: Have you seen the news today?

Catty-Corner: I am not sure. It depends on the news. What is happening?

Me: Do you really not know? You are usually the one who tries to tell me.

Catty-Corner: Well, if the roles were not capable of being reversed then they would not be roles. What is happening?

Me: What is happening is that they are trying to destroy our democracy. It has actually reached that point, and it cannot—

Catty-Corner: Our what?

Me: Our *democracy*.

Catty-Corner: What is that?

Me: Well, it is what we have. It is the fact that they are trying to destroy it that is important, though.

Catty-Corner: Where is this happening?

Me: Well, here, of course. At least mostly, I suppose.

Catty-Corner: The United States is not a democracy, though.

Me: I see what you are saying now. I had thought that you were actually being serious. It is important to remember that just because the idea of American government has been polluted and perverted to the point of nonrecognition does not mean that it has actually been changed. A thing that has become a parody of itself still remains itself, after all, and if we do not have the courage to keep calling it what it is then we have already let the other side win. We cannot allow their madness to become the norm.

Catty-Corner: I see.

Me: That is why I may find your joke funny, but it is dangerous. I know that they have made it seem like the government that we are supposed to have is warped, and if we just shrug our shoulders then they will actually make it that way. They will, in fact, warp things as far as we let them.

Catty-Corner: Can I hear your argument for the fact of a United States democracy?

Me: What do you mean? I just gave it to you.

Catty-Corner: Well, it must have fallen through my hands. It also might have dissipated and floated away while you were giving it over. It did, in fact, seem to be lighter than the air.

Me: Does that mean that you are against democracy?

Catty-Corner: My trouble is in accepting the idea of might making right. It seems monstrous and unembraceable to me, and I cannot imagine—

Me: That is not democracy at all, and the idea of might making right is something that you should *never* accept. Democracy is the thing that keeps people from being crushed by might.

Catty-Corner: Does that mean that democracy is inherently for the little guy?

Me: Of course.

Catty-Corner: Does that mean that a majority is inherently for the little guy?

Me: What do you mean?

Catty-Corner: Well, democracy is the will of the majority, after all. If the little guy ever finds himself in the minority then it is rather obvious that democracy will do nothing for him, and if he ever finds himself in the majority then it is rather obvious that democracy will do everything for him. In a democratic world, after all, the little guy's only hope is to make himself as big as possible at the expense of whatever other little guys there are who are not strong enough to—

Me: You are obviously having trouble with this, and I am not sure why it is something that we are even arguing about. If the little guy is in the right and his arguments are sound then the majority will obviously support him, and that is—

Catty-Corner: How will we be able to know if he is right, though?

Me: Well, by whether the majority supports him, of course.

Catty-Corner: Is that not might making right?

Me: It is *right* making right.

Catty-Corner: I see.

Me: Do you?

Catty-Corner: I am not sure, and I suppose that we can never know. Curse us for not having a third person here.

Me: What do you mean?

Catty-Corner: Well, a third person would allow us to vote. As it is, we will never know which of us is right because we cannot have a vote. Ballot boxes are, after all, the things that you have said fit within keyholes.

Me: Are you still on might making right? I told you that that is not democracy.

Catty-Corner: Are you aware that *might* does not just refer to brawn? When, for example, the pen is said to be mightier than the sword then it does not mean that the former is simply more muscular. In fact, I would say that the state of overly righteous minds is a far more dangerous one than the state of overly sculpted muscles.

Me: It is obvious that you have not been listening to me at all.

Catty-Corner: Have you been listening to me?

Me: Of course. That is how I know that you are wrong. You were the one who simply decided that I was wrong before we even started the conversation, and whatever points I make do not matter to you because you have already decided that you are right.

Catty-Corner: When we are long dead and the future is in the middle of determining our value then I would be willing to bet that one of the chief explainers of our time will be the fact that we could not even correctly term what it was that we were living under. After all, it feels easy to make fun of those who lived in the Roman

Dark Ages, but they, at the very least, were aware that they had kings.

Me: It is good to know that you are against democracy.

Catty-Corner: It is sad to know that you still do not know what democracy is. You define the word by pulling it out of things that you like, and then you use it like a salve that has magical properties. The truth is that if your moral compass is guided by the counting of raised hands then you have a broken one, and it is dreadful to think of where you will lead us by its continued use.

Me: I have to go.

Catty-Corner: Where to?

Me: I am going to the store. That was what I was planning to do before you distracted me, and now I am late.

Catty-Corner: Can you share your argument for democracy with me before leaving.

Me: I really am already late.

Catty-Corner: We did not get to my argument, though. We also spoke the whole time without even mentioning either the government that we are supposed to have or the one that we actually have. We had to spend the whole time ignoring both de jure and de facto in favor of duh.

Me: I really do have to go.

Catty-Corner: Will I see you this evening?

Me: I do not think so.

ON VOTING

Me: Afternoon, neighbor.

My Catty-Corner Neighbor: Good afternoon.

Me: Have you already gotten back? You were here when I left, so I did not expect to still find you here when I returned.

Catty-Corner: I have been here all day.

Me: Does that mean that you will be leaving soon?

Catty-Corner: What do you mean?

Me: Well, are you not going to vote? Today is the day, after all.

Catty-Corner: I never vote. It is one of those—

Me: If you never vote then why do you always complain? You are, after all, one of the biggest complainers that I have ever met, so I always assumed that you must vote. In fact, I assumed that you were one of those who finds a way to vote multiple times. Voting is the very least that a person can do, after all, so to find out that you shirk what should be the most basic and simple of steps is something that I should have—

Catty-Corner: Well, I am unwilling to restrict my stride to the shortest of steps, I suppose.

Me: What do you mean?

Catty-Corner: I mean that I will not vote, no matter how thoroughly you try to bully me into doing so. If the obeyance of an unjust law is itself unjust then is the willful participation in the same not, at the very least, the same? Injustice is to me as inadmissible as the irrelevant, and I never let—

Me: You are not making any sense at all. Injustice is what voting fixes, which is something that everyone knows. If you do not like the way that things are then you are supposed to vote to change them.

Catty-Corner: The truth is that if you want to change the way that things are then you are supposed to *act* in such a way that changes them. It is important to remember that change is that which is merely codified by voting, and when a vote turns a certain way then you can be sure that it was the work of many who had to treat it as already so for a long time.

Me That is not what we are talking about at all. We are talking about you not voting, and you are just trying to come up with excuses.

Catty-Corner: Well, if it is a good one then what is wrong with an excuse? Ignoring a valid excuse is, in fact, a far stupider path than—

Me: You are still trying to avoid—

Catty-Corner: It is important to remember that the initial rallying cry of the United States was that of *No taxation without representation*. If we ignore for a moment that we still allow this very thing then we can look past it and see that we have actually made things even worse. After all, are there not among us those who could make calls for *No taxation without identification*? If being ruled without being heard is bad then is being ruled without so much as a voice not worse? Every purchase of theirs, for example, gets taxed, and they are forced to pay a government that does not allow them to acknowledge the very situation that they are in. We dangle citizenship before them like a carrot on a stick, and we allow them to do all that we—

Me: If you are just going to keep avoiding what I—

Catty-Corner: The truth is that you will not be able to keep on ignoring them forever. There are those who deplore the loss of the *model American* in modern America, but they are incorrect. There still exist many model Americans, but they are, instead, called *immigrants*. The original American *model* was, after all, that of family, faith, and thrift. We ourselves have long given up the last of these, we have long abandoned the first, and do I even need to mention the middle? It is only in immigrants that one can find a whiff of Americanness, and model Americans in the modern world are most consistently those whom we legally bar from the title. One wonders just how much more of the country that they will allow themselves to build before making it theirs, and if you—

Me: I am going inside. It is obvious that you are just trying to twist words so that you will feel better about not voting. You are probably just lazy, I bet, and that is why you do not want to put in the time to vote.

ON EIGHTEEN

Me: Morning, neighbor.

My Catty-Corner Neighbor: Good morning. Is that a book that I see tucked under your arm?

Me: It is. You have a good eye. I have been reading it for the past couple weeks, and I am hoping that I can finish it this afternoon.

Catty-Corner: What is it about?

Me: You would not like it at all. I am certain that you would hate it, in fact. It is a nonfiction book, and I know how you only ever care about novels.

Catty-Corner: Well, I have always found it to be true that philosophers may be the ones who get credit for writing that which gets termed *philosophy*, but it is the good philosophers who turn their words to fiction.

Me: That is just your opinion, and it is obvious to see how prejudiced it is, too. It feels like we go through this same routine every time that we talk, and I am in every instance unfairly checked by your unwillingness to ever check yourself. If you would only—

Catty-Corner: What is your book about?

Me: I already told you that you would not like it. It is a book about history, which I know would be like—

Catty-Corner: I may have read it. What is—

Me: I am willing to bet that you have not read it. It would, after all, challenge your assumptions, and you would be forced to address the fact that you are wrong about a lot of things, which is something that you would never do. You have an idea of the world that is only based on whatever you happen to think of it, so you cannot take the resistance of other ideas since they would shatter your whole worldview. Your situation is obvious to everyone but you.

Catty-Corner: What is one of the more interesting facts that you have come across in the book?

Me: Well, there was actually one just a few minutes ago. It was, in fact, a whole paragraph that I highlighted, and I drew a star in the book's margin, too. It was a section that addressed the history of voting, and the part that I highlighted was about how there used to be people who actually argued that the right to vote should be based upon property ownership. I thought that the author must be exaggerating, but I investigated it myself, and it is true. There were actually people who—

Catty-Corner: What were their reasons?

Me: What do you mean?

Catty-Corner: Well, why did they argue for it?

Me: How can you even ask that when you know that their reasons were bad? The only reason that they argued for it was because they wanted to keep down those without property, which is something that everyone knows. There is not any actual reason that would make sense, after all, so it was just them trying to be archaic so that they could enjoy the fruits that had been stolen for them by prior generations. It is only because you are so stupid that—

Catty-Corner: Is arguing for voters to be property owners actually any more outdated than it would be, for example, to argue for allowing an eighteen-year-old to vote?

Me: What do you mean?

Catty-Corner: I mean that the only metric by which an eighteen-year-old is either an adult or a voter is the one that first views him as an acceptable soldier. It is important to remember that eighteen-year-olds are allowed to vote because their age was at one time determined to be the youngest at which it was deemed acceptable for a citizen to die for his country. What could, after all, be more *archaic* than that?

Me: […]

Catty-Corner: […]

Me: It is never acceptable for a soldier to have to die for his country.

Catty-Corner: That is not what we are talking about at all. It may feel good to you to derail things in your own favor, but such is still a derailment, and it is proof of your inability to—

Me: You are the unable one among us, not me. You are obviously unwell, too.

Catty-Corner: I see.

Me: I am going back inside. I thought that I might be able to come out here to read and learn in peace, but I was obviously wrong.

ON FIFTY

Me: Morning, neighbor.

My Catty-Corner Neighbor: Good morning. Are you able to count?

Me: What do you mean?

Catty-Corner: Well, are you aware of numbers and their relations to one another within the—

Me: Of course, I know how to count. I was confused by your question, though, and it caught me off guard since it is obviously—

Catty-Corner: What part of my question was confusing? There were, after all, only five words, and they were each short and—

Me: I mean that I do not know why you are asking me the question.

Catty-Corner: Why should that matter?

Me: Well, it matters because it helps to know the reason for a question before answering it. If, for example, you were asking me the question to use my answer against me then it would alter what I would say. If, however, it is just an honest question then you are supposed to indicate as much so that the other person can know that he can answer freely. Any animosity that results from not making known the intention of your question is, therefore, your own fault, and you cannot say—

Catty-Corner: Will you prove your numeric ability to me?

Me: What I am going to do is leave, and I will prove it to you, too. I am early for work, but that does not mean that I cannot show up there so. You have proven that all you want to do is to try to insult me, anyway, so it would be stupid—

Catty-Corner: Does that mean that you do not know how to count?

Me: I already told you that I can, which I know that you already know, anyway. All you are—

Catty-Corner: If you so certainly can then why do you not so simply do? Is it that—

Me: Do you really want me to count?

Catty-Corner: Will you?

Me: […]

Catty-Corner: *Can* you?

Me: If it will shut you up then I suppose that it is worth my time to make you look stupid. I want you to know, however, that I am only playing your game because I know how easy it will be to beat you.

Catty-Corner: When will you demonstrate for me your—

Me: Where do you want me to start counting?

Catty-Corner: Wherever you feel the firmest.

Me: One, two, three, four—

Catty-Corner: How about with bigger numbers?

Me: Thirty-five, thirty-six, thirty-seven, thirty-eight—

Catty-Corner: How about with numbers past fifty?

Me: I have, I think, wasted enough—

Catty-Corner: This is my last question, and it is, in fact, the only thing that I am wanting to know.

Me: Fifty-one, fifty-two, fifty-three, fifty-four—

Catty-Corner: I see.

Me: What do you mean?

Catty-Corner: Well, I see that your awareness of numbers does not stop at fifty, which means that I must change my—

Me: I know that you are lying, and you are just trying to make some point that will not make any sense, anyway. I bet that you do not even have—

Catty-Corner: My point is that there must be some reason for our number of states being capped at fifty. There is, after all, no *legal* reason why they should be stopped at that number, so I had thought that it must be because Americans are not confident about any of the numbers past fifty, but that does not seem to be the case, either. Is it simply that rights are supposed to take a backseat to round numbers? It is important to remember that population is supposed to be the greatest determinant of statehood, but the national population has doubled since the addition of any new state, and it has tripled since the addition of any continental one. It is obvious that the addition of new states is both needed and warranted, but those with opposing interests have warped the issue, and they say that it is the Electoral College that is at root of—

Me: That is it. I will not keep standing here and listen to you blame people for something that is the fault of the system. Everyone knows how bad the Electoral College is, and it is the reason why we are forced to live in a society where power is never in the hands of the people. If you support the Electoral College then you must also be one of those who supports Manifest Destiny, and it must be—

Catty-Corner: Is it not odd that those who decry *Manifest Destiny* are those able to so comfortably live within the *Fable of Fifty*? It is important to remember that the purpose of the Electoral College is to ensure that America will always have an American president, and the system assumes that *any* single-state candidate will be as bad for the country as *any* single-issue candidate. There are, after all, quite a few states that a national candidate would never even think about if the Electoral College did not force him to do so, and it is also—

Me: If the Electoral College is so good then why does it allow for a president to be elected with less than fifty-one percent of the overall vote?

Catty-Corner: I see.

Me: What I see is that you have no answer for me. I have proven that your whole argument is only your opinion, and you were probably just expecting that no one would ever challenge it. How, after all, could the Electoral College ever be good when it does not honor the will of the majority?

Catty-Corner: […]

Me: I knew that you would not have a counterargument for me. You know that I am right, so you know that you cannot continue. You were not saying anything important at all, but I was still able to—

Catty-Corner: My point is that more state lines must be drawn or else the very idea of statehood will soon become lost. California, for example, must be split into thirds, and Texas, too, must accept regionhood. Florida should, at the very least, be two states, and then there are all the cases of—

Me: I am going to leave since it is obvious that you are just trying to change the topic. I proved you wrong about the Electoral College, so that is what is important.

Catty-Corner: […]

Me: I will give you some more time to wrap your head around my argument. You can try a counterargument on me whenever you like, but I think that we both know what will happen.

ON GRAVITY

Me: Evening, neighbor.

My Catty-Corner Neighbor: Good evening. It is good to see you.

Me: It is good to see you, too.

Catty-Corner: Do you have a minute to talk before heading inside?

Me: I really do not think so. I am in a hurry, and it is a matter of—

Catty-Corner: It is only one question that I want to ask.

Me: Well, if that is true then I have the time, I suppose.

Catty-Corner: It is only a true-or-false question, too.

Me: I am ready for it.

Catty-Corner: Is gravity a constant?

Me: Of course. Would you prefer if I said *true*, instead? I do not, after all, want to have my grade hurt by wording, even though you did not even word the question correctly yourself.

Catty-Corner: [...]

Me: Was that actually the question? I am not sure whether to believe that it was, and it does, I think, hardly count as one when it is so easy to answer. Even a true-or-false question, after all, is supposed to have *some* level of—

Catty-Corner: Well, your answer to that true-or-false question was wrong, so I—

Me: What do you mean?

Catty-Corner: I mean that your simple answer to that simple question was a wrong one, which simply means that you do not have—

Me: My answer was the obvious one, and it was correct, too. Anyone would tell you the same thing, and most people, in fact, would have answered even quicker than I did since I was having to be worried about whether you were—

Catty-Corner: Well, anyone who answered like you would be wrong along with you, and even the most conniving of curves could not help since they do, after all, only touch grades, not answers. The truth is that gravity is—

Me: I know the truth, and I just told it to you. Everyone knows that gravity is a constant, and I can, after all, remember using it as such back in math class, so that

282

means that it must be so. In fact, it even had its own symbol for quick use in formulas.

Catty-Corner: Is there gravity on the Moon?

Me: Of course.

Catty-Corner: Is that gravity on the Moon the same as the gravity on the Earth?

Me: Of course not.

Catty-Corner: Well, if those two gravities are not the same then how can gravity be a constant?

Me: I am not sure why you are having so much trouble with this. Gravity is a constant, and you can use it that way in math formulas, so that is what is important. Weight, for example, is something that you must have constant gravity to calculate for, and it is, in fact, such a—

Catty-Corner: Does that mean that the gravity on the Earth is constant, even though it may not be the same as the gravity on the Moon? There are, in other words, two constants that we are talking about, which means that the Earth has its constant gravity, and the Moon has its constant own?

Me: That is a good way of putting it, I suppose. They are separate constants, but they are both still constants. Your weight on the Moon, for example, would need to be calculated by multiplying your mass by the gravity on the moon.

Catty-Corner: Well, if we now restrict ourselves to the first of those constants, which is that of the gravity on the Earth, then why is it that all the factors that determine that *constant* are not themselves constant?

Me: I have already told you that the earth's gravity is a constant, and I am not sure how much simpler I can make it. Gravity is used to calculate the nonconstant, not the other way around, which is something that everyone knows.

Catty-Corner: Have you ever heard of the changing tides?

Me: Do you mean in war? It is, I think, usually called *turning the tides*, but it is only—

Catty-Corner: I mean the actual tides, not their metaphors. Have you heard of them?

Me: Of course. I am not sure how much longer I should allow myself to—

Catty-Corner: My point is that the fact of a tide change is itself proof that the Moon's effect on the Earth is *not* constant. After all, every single second of a tide change means that the Moon *must* be changing its effect on the Earth, and this difference should, after all, be expected to cause a difference.

Me: [...]

Catty-Corner: [...]

Me: Have you really never calculated the weight of an object?

Catty-Corner: I have, but the difference is in the—

Me: If you have ever calculated weight then you should know that gravity *must*, by rule, be a constant. It is, in fact, the only way for things to be since you could never know your weight before first using gravity to calculate it.

Catty-Corner: I see.

Me: Well, that is good to hear. My point, has, I think, been proven enough that even you should be able to see how obvious it is that—

Catty-Corner: The truth is that there exists a gravitational constant, but gravity in *any* actuality is *never* a constant. Your weight is a—

Me: Thank you for admitting to having lied. I was going to feel bad about walking away while you were still confused, but if you have just been being as stupid as you usually are then I will, in fact, feel the opposite. Everyone knows that gravity is necessary for your own weight, so it is not something that I should have had to tell you.

Catty-Corner: I see.

Me: Well, I know that you are blind.

ON SHAPE

Me: Afternoon, neighbor.

My Catty-Corner Neighbor: Good afternoon. What is that on your wrist?

Me: It is a hospital bracelet. Thank you for reminding me that I need to take it off.

Catty-Corner: I hope that it is not anything serious.

Me: It was just a checkup. I schedule one whenever they tell me to. I was still sweaty walking in, of course, but I actually left the place feeling better than when I went in.

Catty-Corner: What do you mean?

Me: Well, I mean that I entered the realm of bad or worse news, and I emerged from it with good news. I obviously know how advanced medicine has become, but this doctor was able to make me feel better without a single prescription.

Catty-Corner: Are you sure that you were not prescribed something while you were not looking?

Me: What do you mean?

Catty-Corner: Well, I am not sure. I am attempting to answer the riddle, but it is only a guess. What about your pockets? Did you check them to make sure that the doctor did not slip you a prescription when you were not looking?

Me: Of course. Going through my pockets was the first thing that I did after leaving. It was not my first visit, after all.

Catty-Corner: I see.

Me: I was waiting for a pitch the whole time, but it never came.

Catty-Corner: You still feel better, though?

Me: I do, and the riddle can be explained by the power of words.

Catty-Corner: What do you mean?

Me: Well, it was not exactly words. It was a photo, but it was taken by a photojournalist, which makes it the same thing. A picture is, after all, worth a thousand words, which means that a good picture must be worth whole books.

Catty-Corner: [...]

Me: There was a book that my doctor had on the coffee table of his small reception room, and I looked through it while waiting for my appointment. It was about health through the ages, and there were a lot of old photos in it that caught my attention. One of them was of a group of GIs from before they were sent to the Second World War, and the photo was taken when there were about one hundred of them lined up and ready to take their entrance physicals. They were all shirtless and wearing only boxer shorts, and the photo was not colorized, but it was still striking because every single one of them was either skinny or flabby and either slouching or obviously wanting to. None of them looked like they had ever worked out, and it looked as if they did not take care of themselves at all. I bet that—

Catty-Corner: Well, I suppose that it is true that they were more concerned with others back then.

Me: That is not what I am saying at all. You are just—

Catty-Corner: How did the photo make you feel better?

Me: Well, it made me realize that I was in better shape than every single one of them. They may be the *Greatest Generation*, but none of them had great bodies. Seeing them made me feel better about myself, and it is heartening to know that I may not work out as much as others do but that I still work out far more than previous others did. I always worry that I am not in good enough shape, after all, so seeing how weak they looked made—

Catty-Corner: Did you ask your doctor about any of this?

Me: Of course not. The book was not written by him, after all, so there would not—

Catty-Corner: The truth is that those of the past were in much better shape than we are, and even a whole team of trainers could not catch us up. We mock each other for skipping *leg day*, but it is *brain day* that we have all so thoroughly abandoned that we cannot any longer even reason its importance. It may be true that we are more *shapely* than those of the past, but to say that we are in better shape is proof that one is too stupid to even be able to—

Me: This is a waste of time, and I am going inside. All you are doing is twisting words so that I will seem bad, and you are lucky that I am the type of person who allows you to. If I wanted to then I could beat you up, after all, so you really should be mindful of what you say around me. I know, however, that you will just continue to take advantage of the—

Catty-Corner: The last thing that I want to say is that if you are not able to correctly figure out what you should hit then all those muscles of yours will mean nothing. A muscular impotence is still an impotence, after all, and your big arms will show themselves to be your own binds, which means—

Me: Well, you should get that impotence of yours checked out. You have plenty of time now, in fact.

ON WORKERS

Me: Evening, neighbor.

My Catty-Corner Neighbor: Good evening.

Me: Can you believe how nice it is this evening? It is the kind of night that makes you want to vacation inside your own life.

Catty-Corner: It reminds me of yesterday, and a lot of it is similar to even earlier days, too. You seem to be in a particularly good mood this evening, though.

Me: You can bet on that. I have been fighting for a raise for months, and I finally won today.

Catty-Corner: Congratulations.

Me: Thank you. My boss told me the same thing, in fact.

Catty-Corner: What do you mean?

Me: He congratulated me after our negotiation was over. He knew how underpaid I was, I think.

Catty-Corner: Well, why are you not out celebrating? Celebration is, after all, the proper reply to congratulation.

Me: That is what I am going to do now. The only reason that I came home is to get ready.

Catty-Corner: You came home before going back to your office?

Me: Of course not. Why would I go back to my office?

Catty-Corner: Well, to meet your coworkers. You spent all day with them, so I am not sure why you would come home before meeting back up with them.

Me: I am going out to celebrate with friends, not coworkers. Why would I want to celebrate with my coworkers? That does not make any sense at all.

Catty-Corner: They are happy for you, I bet.

Me: Well, if they knew about it then they might be.

Catty-Corner: What do you mean?

Me: None of my coworkers knows that I got the raise. Some of them know that I have been asking for it, I suppose, but if they heard about me getting it then it did not come from me. My boss asked me not to mention it to anyone since he was making an exception for me. I would not have said anything on my own, of course, since it is not polite to talk about salaries.

Catty-Corner: It is not *polite* on one hand, and it is not *politic* on the same.

Me: [...]

Catty-Corner: [...]

Me: Was that supposed to have been insulting? It would not surprise me at all to find out that you are trying to turn my raise into something about yourself.

Catty-Corner: Well, it does not surprise me at all to find out that you are unable to view it in a way *other* than being about yourself.

Me: I knew it. You are jealous of me, I bet.

Catty-Corner: What am I jealous about?

Me: My raise, I suppose. People can be jealous about anything, so I can tell that you are jealous without having to know what exactly it is that you are jealous about.

Catty-Corner: Do you think that your coworkers are jealous?

Me: If they knew about it then they probably would be.

Catty-Corner: Do you think that they would be angry?

Me: What do you mean?

Catty-Corner: Well, if they were aware of the blow that they have been dealt then would they look for ways to—

Me: That does not make any sense at all. I fought for my raise, and I landed a blow for workers everywhere by getting it.

Catty-Corner: You landed *one* blow for *one* worker here. The truth is that a *worker's* rights are never synonymous with *workers'* rights, and you have made things more difficult for others by way of striving to make them better for only yourself. After all, the extra work that you bargain with today becomes the new expectation for your replacement tomorrow. You yourself may have risen, but the platform that you jumped from has been forced downward by the motion, and the new—

Me: I want to let you know that you can stop trying to upset me. I am in too good a mood for even your most insulting attempts, so it is a waste of your time as well as of mine. I have friends waiting for me, so I am—

Catty-Corner: It is important to remember that the conquest of a worker's rights will *always* come at the expense of workers' rights. Not only did you merely land one blow today, but it was a blow that you delivered on behalf of your employer and directed at your coworkers. You said that your boss told you congratulations, but he should have thanked you, too.

Workers' rights are those that can never be stood for alone, and your willingness to trade them for—

Me: I just told you that you will not be able to upset me, so you really should stop trying. The only thing that you have done is to prove that you are jealous of me, and it is all so—

Catty-Corner: The truth is that fighting for everyone is both difficult and frustrating while fighting for yourself feels so streamlined that those who do the latter convince themselves that all others must simply be stupid. It never occurs to them that there are those who are capable of perceiving life's shortcuts and then spurning them.

Me: Well, there are a lot of things that do not occur to you, and they are almost all important, too. I will not, however, allow you to keep me from my friends any longer, and I really hope that you are not out here when I return from celebrating.

ON TECHNOLOGY

Me: Evening, neighbor.

My Catty-Corner Neighbor: Good evening. What is that that you have with you?

Me: My new phone. I wanted to spend some time learning it before I went to bed.

Catty-Corner: It looks like a watch.

Me: Well, it is. They have now combined the two. You have to wear an ear bud while using it, of course, but that is the only downside.

Catty-Corner: The screen looks like it would be too small. How can you watch anything on it?

Me: It projects an expansion whenever it needs to. The screen on the watch face is just for showing the time and notifications, and it pops up the bigger screen whenever I start using it or when it is playing a video. The bigger screen is not actually there, of course, but it works just like any real one on any other phone, and it works as a touchscreen, too.

Catty-Corner: I cannot remember hearing about this at all. How new is it?

Me: I just got it today. I was able to leave work early since—

Catty-Corner: I mean the technology. You are the first person whom I have seen with it.

Me: Well, this is the first phone with it, and it has only been out for about a month, too. I have been following the news about it ever since it was announced, though, so I have known about it for, at the very least, nine months. I was able to get one because the company who makes them did preorders and then a lottery with the entrants, and I was lucky enough to be in the fourth round of those who were issued one. I am not sure how many they are giving out in each round, but I can promise that everyone is going to have one before too long. Other companies will start knocking-off the technology, too, and then it will just be considered as another thing.

Catty-Corner: Is it really that different?

Me: Can you imagine never having to put your phone in your pocket ever again? Think of all the time that that saves in tiny increments across your whole life. When it is on your wrist then you never have to worry about it. You stop having to worry about leaving it somewhere, you stop having to worry about it falling out of your pocket, and you stop having to worry about anyone stealing it. There are all sorts of other little benefits that I cannot think of right now, too, but not having to use pockets is probably the biggest one. It is one of those things where you cannot even remember how you used to get by before it came along. I cannot now even recall how anyone does without it, and it makes me think—

Catty-Corner: Does it seem like it has—

Me: The thing that I want to say about it before you start on whatever point you have is that it makes me think of how lucky we are, and I mean every single one of us. It is incredible to think of all the incredible changes in technology from even when I was just a kid. It did not use to be this way, of course, and it used to be that people would be forced to live with the same technology for generations, but it feels like we get new things every week. If only they knew—

Catty-Corner: What age do you consider us to be more technologically advanced than?

Me: Well, every single one of them. After all, how many of them had the internet?

Catty-Corner: Well, who cares about second place?

Me: What do you mean?

Catty-Corner: I mean that to say that we are the most advanced is to imply that the *best* that we could put forward would beat the *best* that any other time could put forward, which shows that there—

Me: That is exactly what I am saying. Have you not actually been listening to me? Not only do we have everything that the past had, but we have built upon them, so we have more just as a basic principle. You do not even have to look at it any further than that. It is not their fault, of course, which is why it is good to not think of the whole thing as a competition, and it is important to do things like read about the past without judging them too harshly. In many cases, after all, they were doing their best. The technology that they had yesterday is what we *started* with today, so we are always going—

Catty-Corner: The truth is that technology's *second* place has perhaps proven to be more turbulent as time has progressed, but *first* place has been ever unchallenged. There is no technology more advanced than the brain, after all, and we have been in possession of it for quite some time. We are perhaps more technologically *accumulated* than the past, but we are more technologically advanced than no one. No age has so far advanced in technology beyond any other.

Me: Well, I thought that you were actually trying to be serious today, and I thought that we might have a true discussion. I gave you the benefit of the doubt, too, but all you ever want to do is not make any sense at all. I think that it must have been that you realized that I was in a good mood because of my new phone, so you knew that I would be more willing to—

Catty-Corner: Are you disagreeing with me?

Me: Of course.

Catty-Corner: About what?

Me: About the whole thing. That should be obvious to even you.

Catty-Corner: What is your disagreement?

Me: I already told you that I disagree. Are you really too stupid to be able to listen to the words that are spoken to you? It is an easy thing to do, and all you have to do is to not think of talking for one second, and you will see how obvious everything—

Catty-Corner: If it is so obvious then advance the idea of your own advancement. Share with me your counterargument for how—

Me: That is it. What is *most* obvious here is that you just want to make jokes and try to insult me. I can learn the new features of my phone anywhere, after all, so I think that I will go and do it anywhere that is away from you.

Catty-Corner: Will you tell me your counterargument before you go so that—

Me: Of course not.

Catty-Corner: Well, I await—

Me: I have already stopped listening to you.

ON INCARCERATION

Me: Evening, neighbor.

My Catty-Corner Neighbor: Good evening, though I can tell that I am the only one of us who thinks of it as so.

Me: What do you mean?

Catty-Corner: Well, you have been pacing for the past few minutes, and I can see that your hands are clenched into fists.

Me: Well, both are justified. I feel angry about something that I should be angry about.

Catty-Corner: What do you mean?

Me: If I were to try to explain to you all the intricacies of the issue then it would take too long, and you would probably not let me get there, anyway. It is enough to say that I am angry about prison reform.

Catty-Corner: What do you mean?

Me: You have just given me an example of my meaning. If you do not know what I am talking about then you are part of the problem that I am so angry about. Your fellow citizens are being plucked out of society every single day, but all you care about is yourself. Everyone knows that our prisons are overcrowded, and the point of them is supposed to be to rehabilitate prisoners, so it is obvious that—

Catty-Corner: If *rehabilitation* is the point of prisons then why are they filled with the unlawful?

Me: What do you mean?

Catty-Corner: Well, a citizen becomes a prisoner following the proceedings of a court, and those court proceedings are, after all, based upon guilt, not need. If the *point* is to rehabilitate then why is the need for rehabilitation not a crime, and why do we send to prison those guilty by evidence rather than by evaluation? If, in other words, rehabilitation is the actual point then why is it never the actual reason?

Me: You are not making any sense at all. Everyone knows that rehabilitation is a good thing, so there is not any reason to be against it.

Catty-Corner: I see.

Me: If you actually took the time to see what prisoners experienced in prison then I bet that you would not be so happy to have them sent there. You are probably one of those who likes it that way, though, since it means that they can be hidden from you so that you do not—

Catty-Corner: Does society need changing?

Me: How can you interrupt me to ask that? Of course, society needs changing, and that is why I am so angry about prisons. I should not have to always repeat—

Catty-Corner: Well, if you believe so strongly in rehabilitation then have you ever considered whether it is *you* who needs it rather than society? Have you not, in other words, questioned whether your belief in rehabilitation is the thing that should be rehabilitated? I am sure that we can find someone who is willing to do the job for you, and if you start to get cold feet then just remember that even they will soon be rehabilitated away.

Me: You are not making any sense at all, and I know that you are just trying to make me scared about something so that I will not—

Catty-Corner: My point is that the only difference between *rehabilitation* and *brainwashing* is the connotations that you apply to the two terms. After all, any *true* rehabilitation can only come from within, so that which comes from without *must*, by rule, be false. The truth is that the purpose of prisons is the carrying out of lawful decrees, and this is the reason why judges and juries spend so much time investigating crimes rather than contenting themselves with characters. To declare rehabilitation to be the *point* of prisons means that they have to become places where the prisoner is molded to society's will before being allowed back out. To be rehabilitated is, after all, to be changed, and no prisoner should ever feel as if his rehabilitation is a prerequisite of his release. Deciding a prisoner's rehabilitation for him is itself, therefore, a cruel and unusual punishment.

Me: Having to listen to your stupid ideas is itself a cruel and unusual punishment to me, and they do not even make any sense at all, anyway. Everyone knows that prisons are overcrowded, so that is what is important.

Catty-Corner: The truth is that it may be true that overcrowded prisons are sad to see, but the eventual appearance of *empty* prisons will be terrifying. After all, any society that values both liberty and law must reconcile itself to some transgression upon both, and empty prisons will either mean that liberty triumphed over law to the point of making the latter have no effect or that law triumphed over liberty to the point of making people too servile to ever transgress. If both bounds and the pushing of them are desirable then the crossing of them becomes inevitable, and if you want society to have its progressors then you must be willing to stomach its transgressors. Progress without some regress is impossible, and there can never be rigorous stirring without some inevitable spilling. After all, even the most necessary and desired change is still, by rule, an infringement upon whatever it happens to supplant.

Me: The only reason that you are saying all this is because you have never been to prison. The examples that you care about are only ever those that happened to you, and it is all so selfish that I cannot—

Catty-Corner: The truth is that saying that another person in his limited time on earth needs *any* conformation to your own limited time on earth is one the most selfish things that you could ever say, and it is a crime that will brand you forever.

Me: You have just proven the fact that you have not been listening to me. I am in favor of *rehabilitation*, not *conformation*.

Catty-Corner: I see.

Me: [...]

Catty-Corner: [...]

Me: Well, I will give you some time alone to see even better. I have been outside long enough, anyway, I think.

ON DESERVATION

Me: Evening, neighbor.

My Catty-Corner Neighbor: Good evening. It is good to see you. I have a story for you that I have been waiting to tell all day. It is something that I can still hardly believe happened, and I know that you will find it interesting. I went to the grocery store this morning, and there was one checkout line that was longer than all the others. In fact, it stretched farther than I could see, and I assumed that it was the only one open, so I was ready to be annoyed, but there were a number of other lines that were clearly open when I returned to the front of the store for checkout. The longer line was, however, still longer than all the others, which did not make any sense, and it even seemed like it was longer than when I had first seen it walking in, which made even less sense. I entered one of the shorter lines, of course, but I kept looking back at the longer one to see if there was a reason why people kept going into it, and I saw—

Me: I really do not deserve it.

Catty-Corner: […]

Me: I do not deserve it at all.

Catty-Corner: What do you mean?

Me: [...]

Catty-Corner: Are you okay over there?

Me: Of course. Why would you even ask that? I am obviously standing here just fine and—

Catty-Corner: Well, you did not reply to me, so I was—

Me: Do you mean that you realized that I was not listening to you then assumed that something must be wrong with me? That does, I suppose, sound like you, and it makes—

Catty-Corner: What is it that you do not deserve?

Me: What do you mean?

Catty-Corner: Well, you said that you do not deserve it, and I am wondering what *it* is.

Me: I was talking to myself.

Catty-Corner: Well, I am interested in what you have to say.

Me: If that is actually true then I will tell you. I do not, of course, believe you, but I am willing to give you a chance, though you obviously do not deserve one. What happened is that I—

Catty-Corner: How do you know that I do not deserve a chance?

Me: Well, because I have had conversations with you before, and you always act like you are being genuine, but you are almost always lying.

Catty-Corner: That alone cannot determine what I *deserve*, though. After all, the least-lying liar is the liar least deserving of the name, and there must, in other words, be two for one to first deserve just as there must be more than one data point before there can ever be one line.

Me: That does not make any sense at all. I know that you are just trying to—

Catty-Corner: The truth is that to say that you do not deserve something is the same as saying that someone else *does* deserve it, and if there exists a possible outcome then there must exist someone who deserves it. Imagine, for example, if you and I were locked inside a room together, and then a—

Me: I already do not like the situation.

Catty-Corner: Imagine if a gunman then joins us. This gunman first proves to us that his weapon is loaded, and then he points it at our heads, and he says that one of us *must* die.

Me: […]

Catty-Corner: Well, which of us should it be?

Me: How can you even ask that question? It is something that you should not even want to think about, but you, I bet, like the idea of—

Catty-Corner: It is important to remember that our hypothetical is not one of me asking but rather the gunman telling, so it is, therefore, unfair to try to save yourself by socially sacrificing me. The truth is that each and every outcome *must*, by rule, be deserved by one of its participants, and to declare otherwise is to sneer in the face of reality. After all, each of us may not be a bad person, so it could be that neither of us is actually deserving of the gunman's bullet, but one of us must be *more* deserving of it than the other. If there exists a certain outcome then there must certainly exist one deserving of it, and if one of us *must* die then one of us *must* deserve to do so.

Me: No one *ever* deserves to die, and everyone knows that.

Catty-Corner: I see.

Me: I should not have to tell you these—

Catty-Corner: My point is that an appeal for oneself is itself an appeal against others. To say, for example, that you are deserving of happiness means that you are simultaneously saying that someone else is not. After all, the state of unhappiness must be a possible one for you to first be able to say that you are above it, and if it is, in fact, an outcome then its space must be filled, which means that someone *must*, by rule, be deserving of it. In other words, to regard your happiness as deserved is the same as to condemn others' unhappiness as the same, and you can never say that you deserve the positive without indicating that someone else deserves the negative.

Me: I am going to go back inside since it is obvious that you are not listening to me. I just told you that no one *ever* deserves to die, and the only type of person who would say otherwise is someone who—

Catty-Corner: It is important to remember that it is impossible for each of something to ever all deserve the same thing, no matter what it is. If different outcomes exist then overarching deservation never can. Take, for example, the millions who have had their lives ended by way of being tortured to death. The existence of their deaths proves that being tortured to death is a potential outcome of life, and it also, therefore, proves that there must be those who deserve this ending. After all, just because those unfortunates happened to have been tortured to death does not in itself prove that they deserved it. Instead, we must compare their lives with the lives of others, and we can then dole out deservation appropriately. In other words, one who died by way of torture may actually have been deserving of death by way of old age, and one who—

Me: I have already repeated myself once that no one *ever* deserves to die, so I will not do it again. If I leave then maybe my message will get through to you, but I have my doubts that you would even be able to—

Catty-Corner: The truth is that if you can find for me a man *underserving* of death then I will show you a man who died long ago. You will, after all, have to—

Me: Well, I suppose that we will just have to wait and see what happens to you.

ON RETARDATION

Me: Evening, neighbor.

My Catty-Corner Neighbor: Good evening. It is nice to see you, but I must let you know that I am not in the mood to talk.

Me: I am sorry to hear that. Did you have a bad day?

Catty-Corner: It was not my day that was the problem. Instead, there was a single hour today that feels as if it will spoil all my remaining years. It is, in fact, something that feels as if it is reaching back to spoil past years, too.

Me: What do you mean?

Catty-Corner: I stopped by a nursing home this afternoon. I was not there long, but it was long enough to envy those who never go. I have always tried to be—

Me: It is those who never go who are the ones most guilty for the place seeming bad to visit.

Catty-Corner: Well, that is just an example of blaming the victim. It is not, after all, the fault of the young that we avert our eyes from that which is both deplorable and our future. We look away from the old because we can tell where they have been headed, and they, in fact, look away from us for the same reason. To see the way that we now expire as if having past some expiration date is a sight that any would be quick to—

Me: I am willing to let you vent about your bad day, but if you just want to say mean things that are also stupid then I am going to leave. I am not even sure who you are mad at, anyway.

Catty-Corner: My point is that I went to a nursing home today, and it made me think about those who are in them. There is, I bet, a—

Me: You are not saying anything important at all. If all you think is that it is sad to see the passage of time then—

Catty-Corner: My point is not that they have become alienated from time but rather that they became alienated from *themselves* long ago. Everyone, after all, eventually grows old, but it is only we now who do not grow at all, and we die as enfeebled as we were born. It is important to remember that if you regard reality as existing no farther than your own ears then reality itself will seem to be collapsing whenever you eventually reach the time of your own demise. If you believe yourself to be life then how, after all, could you ever face death? The tradeoff for the unexamined life is a glassy-eyed death, and the things that you ignore in favor of ease today will be the very things that rise up to doom you upon the sight of that first wrinkle tomorrow. I saw this very afternoon the eyes of those who had lived such lives and had endured such collapse, and it made me hate our gaping, worldwide plunge into the retarded while at the—

Me: What did you just say?

Catty-Corner: I was saying that I stopped by a nursing home this afternoon, and it made—

Me: That is not what I am talking about.

Catty-Corner: What do you mean?

Me: You know what you did.

Catty-Corner: […]

Me: […]

Catty-Corner: I used the word *retarded*.

Me: You just said it again.

Catty-Corner: Well, why does the number of uses matter?

Me: If you say it even one time then that is too many.

Catty-Corner: Is it a dangerous word?

Me: It is a bad word.

Catty-Corner: Well, so is *bad*, but we still condescend to use it when appropriate.

Me: That does not make any sense at all. It is obvious that you are just trying to not make sense so that I will get mad, and you want me to—

Catty-Corner: That anger of yours would, I think, be more usefully directed at retardation itself rather than making it seem—

Me: I am going to leave if you say the r-word again. I said that I was willing to let you vent about your bad day, which means that I was already being generous, so you should, I think, stop trying so hard to—

Catty-Corner: The truth is that we are all the r-word, and so long as it remains such then so shall we. One can, in fact, clearly trace the way in which the word has been progressively forced underground in step with our freefall toward it. We are unable to face that which we have done to ourselves, so we kill the messenger by way of banishing the word. There is not, after all, a better example of—

Me: All you are doing is proving how stupid you are, and you have not been making any—

Catty-Corner: It is important to remember that the descent of man is always closely followed by his offended denial of any such movement, though being the r-word does, after all, free you from the responsibility of recognizing it.

Me: […]

Catty-Corner: […]

Me: If anyone is the r-word then it is you, not me.

Catty-Corner: I see.

Me: What I see is that it is time for me to stop wasting my time. You are obviously too stupid to be able to—

Catty-Corner: If you have not liked what I have said then simply go pour some sugar down your throat, some flashing colors into your eyes, and some loud noise into your ears. It will then not be long before you find that retardation of yours holding you as close as ever, and the two of you can continue on hand in hand until—

Me: I told you that I would leave if you said the r-word again, and I know that if I keep giving you more chances then you will just keep abusing them. You were informed of what was not allowed, so the only thing that you have proven is that you are too stupid to follow directions.

ON INFINITY

Me: Morning, neighbor.

My Catty-Corner Neighbor: Good morning. Is it still last night for you, though?

Me: Well, it is still last night for just about everyone. The bars have only been closed for a little over half an hour, after all.

Catty-Corner: Is that where you have been?

Me: Not this time. I just had a few friends over, instead. I suppose that you could say that we have been turning my place into a bar.

Catty-Corner: Have they all gone home?

Me: Of course not. We are all still going strong. I just needed to come out and get some air.

Catty-Corner: What a thing to need.

Me: Why are you up and out so early?

Catty-Corner: I could not sleep.

Me: I hope that it has not been from us being too loud.

Catty-Corner: It has not been from that at all. Instead, it is from all the noise that is coming from everything else. It is a fairly regular issue for me.

Me: I am sorry to hear that.

Catty-Corner: A big part of it is just age, I think. That clock that sits inside each of us eventually becomes like a watch with a low battery in that it continues to count the seconds while aware that each next tick could be the one carrying doom. It feels cynical and defeatist, but what else is there for the thing to do? It is a clock and cannot help from counting, and you are finite and cannot help from dying.

Me: Is that how it is pronounced? *Finite*? I always thought that the word started out sounding like *fin* rather than *fine*. I just assumed it was said the same way as infinite, I suppose, and—

Catty-Corner: Do not say that word.

Me: What word? *Infinite*?

Catty-Corner: Of course. Keep it from me.

Me: What do you mean?

Catty-Corner: That word, nothing is worse than it.

Me: Well, could it not be said that nothing is but it?

Catty-Corner: What do you mean?

Me: Well, the universe is infinite, after all.

Catty-Corner: It is?

Me: That is what I have always heard. It makes sense, too.

Catty-Corner: You have been *told* that it makes sense, which is a different thing. The truth is that if the universe is in fact the i-word then sanity is a joke. It is impossible for there not to be encompassing madness in a limitless universe.

Me: What do you mean?

Catty-Corner: Well, what do you think the odds were for life as we currently know it to have become life as we currently know it?

Me: Do you mean if I was betting beforehand?

Catty-Corner: That is a fair way of looking at it. In other words, what percent chance would you have given reality for having become reality, and this includes all the way down to the distinction between which foot you currently have forward while standing?

Me: Low.

Catty-Corner: *How* low?

Me: I am not sure that I could say how low.

Catty-Corner: Would you say higher than zero percent, though?

Me: Of course.

Catty-Corner: Well, that is all we need. With the i-word then anything able to occur *must* do so, and everything that does occur *must* also repeat. If a thing's odds are over zero then the i-word must include it as well as continuing copies of it. The i-word is not simply the numbers one, then two, then three, and then on for forever. Instead, it is one, then all possible repeats of one, then two, then all possible repeats of two, then three, then all possible repeats of three, and then on for forever. The i-word is every interval as well as every iteration of every interval. The i-word is forever in *every* direction, not simply the direction that you happen to be measuring. There can never be limited outcomes on an unlimited scale.

Me: I think that I am able to follow what you are trying to say. What do you mean, though?

Catty-Corner: Well, imagine a pile of jellybeans. This pile includes every jellybean currently in existence, and each jellybean is also numbered so that it is unique from every other. If I were to tell you to select any two jellybeans from anywhere in this pile, record their numbers, and return them back to the pile then would this be a possible task?

Me: Of course.

Catty-Corner: What if I were to tell you to select again?

Me: Of course. That would not—

Catty-Corner: Does that mean that it would be a simple and easy task to continue selecting pairs, recording their results, and perhaps even attempting to analyze all the returning data?

Me: Of course.

Catty-Corner: What if we were to then introduce the i-word to the game?

Me: What do you mean?

Catty-Corner: Well, what if I told you to keep making the selections an i-word number of times?

Me: […]

Catty-Corner: Do you not have an answer?

Me: I was waiting for you to finish the question. All you are doing is repeating the same thing, so I do not think that an answer is even needed from me.

Catty-Corner: The introduction of the i-word does not change your answer or give you the slightest pause? It is the thing that even gods tremble in the face of, after all.

Me: It does not seem so bad to me.

Catty-Corner: Well, if we went back to our jellybeans then what would you say would happen the first time that you pulled out the same pair from a previous selection?

Me: What do you mean?

Catty-Corner: Well, is it something that you would celebrate? Would you fall down on your knees in reverence of what you had witnessed? It is important to remember that selecting the same two jellybeans as a previous selection would be a realization of odds so outrageous that our minds would struggle to comprehend the smallness of the numbers involved.

Me: Well, if I knew that the selections were never going to end then I would not be surprised by the fact that a duplicate selection eventually happened.

Catty-Corner: Why not?

Me: Because there are only so many jellybeans.

Catty-Corner: Does that mean that limited outcomes on an unlimited scale necessitate repetition?

Me: Of course.

Catty-Corner: *Of course?*

Me: *Of course*. You are not saying anything special. You usually say nothing at all, but this is just nothing special.

Catty-Corner: It is important to remember that you must apply the thing that you accept. It should be obvious that once selecting this first set of duplicate jellybeans then you will eventually select another, and you will even eventually select the same selection as your first duplicate pair, and then you will do it again, too. Once your selections reached the point where we no longer have names for their numbers then we would be able to see with better perspective, though this better perspective itself would still be only a further shade of the i-word's actual perspective. As our selections continued and gained us further insight then we would be able to see the places where a selection was duplicated for the fourth, fifth, and more times, and we would be able to see runs of the same series of selections, and we would be able to see patterns of series of runs, and we would be able to find gigantic sections of selections that were matches with gigantic sections elsewhere, and we would not be able to ever—

Me: Do you have a point? I have been out here long enough, I think, and I want to get back inside.

Catty-Corner: My point is that nothing can be the i-word without repeating itself, and this repetition cannot occur across a limitless range without causing unlimited repetitions. Uniqueness in an i-word universe is impossible, and a single occurrence is thus definitive proof of recurrence.

Me: I still do not understand why you are so scared of the word.

Catty-Corner: Well, as a clinger to sanity then I understand that the i-word is the most potent of attacks on it.

Me: […]

Catty-Corner: The best way to see what I mean is to point into the sky.

Me: What do you mean?

Catty-Corner: Point into the sky.

Me: Do you actually want me to lift my arm and point?

Catty-Corner: Is that okay?

Me: You only have about ten seconds before I go back inside.

Catty-Corner: Well, will you point into the sky for them?

Me: I am pointing into the sky. What now? Is there supposed to be some—

Catty-Corner: All that is left is to realize what you are doing.

Me: What do you mean?

Catty-Corner: Well, think about what is pointing back at you. It does not matter where in the sky you point because out there in the direct path of your finger is another finger pointing back at you, and this second finger belongs to a hand just like yours that has just been given the same direction as you. There *must* be an i-word number of yous, and each is a distinct clone without being a copy. Point your finger and realize that many other fingers that could be yours are pointing back. Point your finger and remember that separating it from one of its many, many disparate twins is not some cross-dimensional gateway or trick of science fiction but, instead, nothing more than plain, old distance.

Me: Are you done? I did not want to start inside while you were still talking.

Catty-Corner: I am done.

Me: Then I will see you tomorrow. It will actually be later today, I suppose. I am going to try to get up by noon, but we will see.

AFTERWORD TO THE FINAL EDITION

Now that two years have passed since the initial posting of my recordings from my conversations with my catty-corner neighbor, I have decided to do so no more. A second year has only confirmed my concerns from the first, and this continuance has made clear the fact that there are those who will ever persist in their choices of wrongness, no matter the quality or quantity of the tools employed to turn them otherwise. This edition will, therefore, be the last addition that I make to the preservation of the stupidity of my time, and I have, I think, fulfilled both my original intention as well as my accepted burden such that no failures can be justly attributed to me.

As part of my determination to end, I have decided that it will be useful to supply a few answers to some of the many questions that I frequently receive, and in this way, I can hopefully put a stop to the practice. The below questions, however, should be not regarded as direct reprints of any that I have received, but, instead, I have composed a collage of the general nature of the inquiries, and they are not intended to answer all that I am asked but rather to preempt the need for the questions themselves. Before, therefore, any attempt to reach out to me, the reader should first consult with the below to find out whether the spirit of what he wants to know has already been detailed, and this will, I think, finally put an end to things.

Q: *Who are you?*

A: My name is Mike Cole, but I will not say anything more. It is best to think of me as just another of the many who are victims of those like my neighbor, though it is a victimization that we do not accept and will not stand for.

Q: *How long have you known your neighbor, or who is he?*

A: I will not allow myself to reveal any personal information about my neighbor. Were our roles reversed, I know that he would not hesitate to give out my very address, but I will not stoop to the levels that he inhabits.

Q: *Why is your book not better written?*

A: Because I did not write it. I type up the recordings of my conversations with my neighbor, and that is all.

Q: *Why do you not take the time to show your neighbor why he is wrong?*

A: I do. I will admit that my frustration with my neighbor often forces me to stop short of full explanations for him, but the above pages prove that I give him much of my time. The reader also does not see every single one of our conversations, so he who asks such a question is he who does not know what he is talking about.

Q: *Why do you allow your neighbor to draw you deeper into his ideas when there are many times when you could have saved yourself from them?*

A: I ask myself this very question after nearly every conversation that I have with my neighbor, and I accuse myself with words very much like these.

Q: *Why is there no conversation about the Conversations?*

A: Because my neighbor is not aware of them, and I have even been able to keep my recordings a secret from him. If I were to tell him about the Conversations then I know that he is one of those who would only care about the money that he could get from the book, so there is no point in my doing so.

Q: *Are there further Conversations, and when will they be released?*

A: My arguments with my neighbor have occurred nearly daily for as long as I can remember, and there are thus many that I have recorded but never transcribed. These extra materials will soon be destroyed since they no longer have any potential value, but the reader can be assured that those not here were still each evaluated by me, and I chose to include the conversations that best fit the purpose of showing through my neighbor.

Q: *Why are you quitting?*

A: I am not quitting. Instead, I am tired of having my time wasted by trying to correct those who are taken in by my neighbor. There has been no end to the thanklessness of this task, and questions like this have only made it worse. I know, however, that there are those out there who are able to see through my neighbor just as easily as I do, so I have the satisfaction of knowing that I leave all others in the hands of these.